Supping At God's Table:

A Handbook for the Domestication of Wild Trees for Food and Fodder

Dr. Elaine M. Solowey

Front cover photo credits: Ido Golandsky, Geoffrey Hobson, and Elaine Solowey
Figure 1: World Climate Map (http://www3.shastacollege.edu/dscollon/images/Maps-Images/world_climate_map.jpg
Figure 3: Shea Tree (http://www.thesheaproject.org/sheatree.html)

ISBN 0-9785565-1-8

The Thistle Syndicate is a group of writers and researchers who are dedicated to bringing specific skills and information to the public in a series of low cost publications.

The publication of this book was supported by the Rosenzweig Coopersmith Foundation.

Biblio Books Israel, Acco O Biblio Books International, Miami
http://www.bibliobooks.com Oemail info@bibliobooks.com

To Edward and Vivian who have made my work possible.

And to my husband Michael, my friend Paula Keys and Professor Arthur Liberman who helped turn my manuscript into a book

Small Steps Towards Abundance
Crops for a More Sustainable Agriculture

Dr. Elaine M. Solowey

Also by Elaine Solowey:
Small Steps Towards Abundance: Crops for
a More Sustainable Agriculture
ISBN 0-9729545-4-14
The shops and supermarkets of the developed world paint a false picture of abundance. Acres of shelves contain every
prepared food imaginable. There are thousands of square miles of glistening perfect to
the eye fruits and vegetables and endless
displays of refrigerated meat. Why then
should we worry about food? Actually these
sights are like a painted screen that hides a
desolate landscape. The abundance of the
supermarket is a false one. In truth much of
humanity is chronically, mercilessly hungry.

Table of Contents

List of Figures

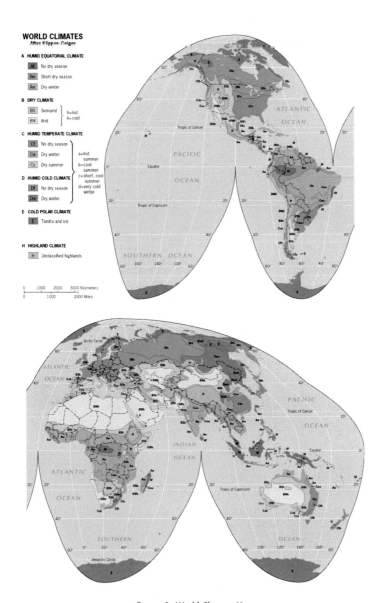

Figure 1: World Climate Map

Supping At God's Table:

A Handbook for the Domestication of Wild Trees for Food and Fodder

Introduction

The title of this book comes from an expression heard in Zimbabwe: When there is nothing to eat at home and a person goes out into the bush to look for food it is said that he or she is supping at God's table.

Indigenous fruit and nut trees are an undervalued resource, ignored and neglected for many years by the scientific and economic powers but often a mainstay and a lifesaver for those with no money.

The African child who goes out with an empty belly to tend the herd finds his breakfast in the bush. The old woman in Appalachia "getting by" on a meager pension in the land of plenty turns the wild berries of the forest slopes into preserves for the pantry and sells a few jars to passing tourists. The laborer who earns only enough to buy dull staple foods finds needed vitamins in the leaves and fruit of plants that hold no interest to the well fed.

The fact that these plants are used and needed by some of the world's poorest people is enough reason to study, promote and preserve IFT.

But there are other pressing reasons. The development of IFT resources could have global impact.

- Recognition and study of the value of IFT products could guarantee that a certain percentage of land would be kept in forest or woodland. There would be an economic rationale for the preservation of rare and endangered IFT species.
- Many cultivated trees have lost much of their genetic diversity and with it disease resistance, tolerances and vigor. Wild relatives of these crops may provide transferable traits for the renewal of weary conventional cultivars.

- IFT trees are often key species in the attempts to restore lost forests or woodlands.
- New crops or cropping systems built on IFT may create employment, reclaim marginal land, provide a base for small scale and cottage industry and increase the food supply where it is most needed: *in impoverished rural areas.*

Because of IFT's precarious position and immense potential the plants must be studied thoroughly, utilized sensibly, developed wisely and protected from harm.

It is in rural areas, among the people who most need IFT that most of the work is being done.

This handbook was written to make the process of domestication, propagation and development of IFT a little easier.

It is dedicated to all those who need, eat, value and love the fruits, nuts and products of the wild.

Let us remember always, that all of us are guests at God's table.

Chapter One
The Importance of Indigenous Fruit Trees (IFT)

The root causes of hunger in the world are complex and no easy answers found for the multitudes who have no money to buy food and cannot raise food for themselves.

But in many areas the fruits and products of the wild mitigate poverty and hunger, providing food during times of food insecurity, bringing in a little money when employment is unavailable and cash is hard to earn.

IFT is in essence a resource that gives the rural poor a chance to go out and get fruit, nuts, wood, salable material or rare substances for themselves and use them to better their lives.

It is no wonder that the rural poor turn to the bush and the forest when times are hard...

IFT resources are used by the world's most impoverished citizens. Their availability can be a matter of life and death.

But the undervalued indigenous trees are at risk in a world where forests are cut down for timber and the jungle cleared for short—term agricultural projects.

The argania tree of Morocco, a valuable source of edible oil, browse and poles is cut down so that orange trees can be planted. Or the marula tree, a veritable supermarket of usable material is felled so that apples may be cultivated.

The imported trees have status and recognized economic importance.

But the lost IFT species were native to the area. They survived without cultivation or irrigation. They were resistant to the local diseases and pests and attuned to local conditions and weather events. The indigenous trees belonged to their areas the way no imported cultivated tree can.

Why are indigenous plants so little known and so little appreciated? Is it not logical to look for a solution to an area's agricultural problems within that area's natural plant resources?

Could it be, for instance, that the solution to African hunger will be found in African plants?

This leads us to an important question about priorities and land use.

I do not ask why we want to grow apples and oranges but rather why we do not utilize such trees the argania of Morocco (Argania spinosa) and marula of southern Africa (Sclerocarya caffra)—trees that have the double advantage of being indigenous and extant.

The conventional answer is that it makes economic sense to plant the imported trees despite the trouble and expense of clearing land and imposing an alien pattern on it—because apples and oranges are valuable fruits while marula and argania are not.

This is not an answer but an excuse.

Marula fruits have more vitamin C than oranges, can be made into Value Added Products (VAP) such as brandy, marmalade, sweets and kamaradin (fruit leather) which are very valuable indeed. And the fruits fall from trees with a plethora of other uses.

The argania tree is a source of animal food, building material (its nickname is ironwood) and one of the finest edible oils in the world.

It cannot be denied that the apples and oranges have much more commercial value than the IFT species because there is no developed market for the fruit or VAP of either argania or marula and no established systems for handling and making the products.

But in a hungry world with agricultural systems plagued by loss of crop diversity, loss of jobs, plummeting farm populations and a looming shortage of good quality water the logical step is to develop both the market and the production systems to utilize the wild crops—not to eliminate them and plant more apples and oranges.

Domesticating IFT, that is including IFT in the continuum of human use, is not as difficult a task as many make it out to be. Most IFT species are known by indigenous people and there is considerable local knowledge of the life cycle and the uses of the plants. This of course is the first step AND second step in the process of domestication.

It does not necessarily mean that the every IFT species is destined for the formal orchard of identical trees and the modern supermarket.

There are many stations along the road to domestication and some IFT species are better left in a wild or semi wild state.

But there are also some plants that will travel the entire route, and become the new orchards and plantations of the 21st century.

And all IFT resources should be considered vital in the struggle against hunger.

Chapter Two
A Few Words About Domestication

Domestication begins for IFT species the instant a human being eats, gathers or uses indigenous fruit, nuts or products. Human beings are very efficient seed spreaders and have had a profound effect on plant populations in prehistoric times merely by passing through an area.

In the many centuries since the dawn of agriculture human influence and activity have transformed the plant population on much of the globe.

This is also the case with IFT species.

People harvest and carry fruit for long distances, spreading seeds out of the species native range and giving other people an opportunity to taste or buy IFT.

Some individuals plant seeds acquired in this manner in home gardens, swap promising wild plants with their neighbors or go into wild areas to bring seeds and seedlings out for their own use.

Somewhere in the large and diverse plant kingdom there may be an IFT species that no one uses or knows about.

That is the theoretical starting point for the scale of Wildness/ Domestication.

Stages of Domestication
The theoretical starting point:
A. No human influence on the population of plants.
1. The plants are undisturbed, undomesticated and unknown

2. The plants are wild, known but not used.

The stages of hunting and gathering

B. By wild crafting (gathering the wild harvest in a sustainable manner) and extractivism—human influence changes the population

1. The plants are wild but known and used in situ
2. The plants are wild, known, fruit is collected for use elsewhere
3. The plants are wild but protected and managed
4. The plants are wild but collected material is extensively traded
5. The plants are wild but over—utilized and in danger

Steps toward domestication

C. Cusp plants(plants on the margins of cultivated land) include both wild and semi domesticated plants

1. Wild populations are culled in a conservatory manner
2. Wild populations are replanted or reseeded after harvest
3. Individual trees or stands of trees are owned
4. Trees are not removed from cleared or cultivated land
5. Trees are not removed from gardens or households

The domestication process

D. The plant population near human settlements becomes domesticated

1. Plants are deliberately introduced to gardens and households
2. Plants are introduced to communities or commons
3. Fruit/nuts/other are harvested in an organized manner

4. Fruits/nuts/other have local value
5. Local VAP and IFT crafts or medicines are traded.

Forest management and organized agriculture

E. Superior individuals of the IFT species enter the agricultural continuum.

1. The trees are desired in agroforestry formats
2. Promising trees are planted in small integrated orchard formats
3. Selection, breeding and grafting occurs locally
4. Selected trees are planted in small plantation formats
5. Selected individuals of the species are propagated and planted in organized orchards and plantations.

Some IFT species will enter the agricultural continuum and go on to become crops as "tame" and valued as the oranges and apples. Others will remain semi—domesticated "included" trees and others ideally will be protected in their wild state. Each stage of domestication has both advantages and disadvantages.

Wild Crop. Wild crops are harvested from natural forest, veldt or arid areas where there is a large population of the tree or plant. These areas are known as the primary source or native range of the wild crop. Here are the centers of biodiversity for the wild crop, for variability, resistance genes, and tolerances as well as the initial source of seeds, cuttings and plants. Wild cropping zones have many developmental possibilities besides the wildcrafting of fruits, nuts and plant material. Among these possibilities: the collection of promising phenotypes, observation of life cycle, the search for plant parasites and diseases, mapping of plant requirements for moisture, soil, light, altitude and early indication of possible problems.

The advantages are great; there are no inputs except for the work expended to collect the IFT products and their transport. There are great variations in size, taste, shape, hardiness, tolerances, keeping qualities and resistances in a wild population. Usually local people know how to use the IFT products and can lead a researcher to the best trees relative to hardiness, taste and size. Local people often know the way to turn the IFT products into something useful, such as jam, alcohol, kamaradin or oil.... (See Figure 8 on page 223.)

The disadvantages: there may be a low yield per measured area, non—uniformity in the IFT product and pressure by government and other institutions to turn the wild area into "productive" land. Additional problems include low trade value for many IFT products, no recognition of IFT as food outside of a limited area and over use of the wild crops in times of famine.

It is important to preserve some areas in a wild state as a gene bank for the species; Valuable genes are easily lost in domesticated formats.

Included trees. These plants have been left on cleared farmland or allowed to grow in areas under cultivation because of their value to the farm, farm family or farm animals. The trees that are "included" usually have a high yield of fruit, nuts or leaves or produce multiple useful materials such as bark poles or thatch. Shade trees, apiary trees and windbreaking trees are often included as well as arboreal medicinals and ornamentals. (See Figure 7 on page 223.)

Only the best trees are spared when land is cleared. This stage of domestication is important because of the discovery and preservation of superior individual trees which are then spread from neighbor to neighbor or relative to relative across the species' native range and sometimes beyond.

The **advantages** of having a handy source of food and material from a tree that needs little input and no care are obvious. Developmentally the included trees are halfway up the road to domestication since selection has already been done by the farmer or gardener. IFT species close to the dwelling are sometimes nourished with the households waste water and compost. Overripe or damaged fruit may feed pigs or chickens. The produce often enters the local market or is bartered among friends and neighbors. (See Figure 3 on page 221.)

Disadvantages: The products of the included trees are usually only used and recognized in the immediate area, collection and trade of products is haphazard, trees are almost always seedlings so there is a good deal of variability in the size and quality of fruit and the harvest index in general.

But these "dooryard trees" may substantially change the standard of living of a family, providing much needed high vitamin food or salable material for cash or trade.

Local Integration

Food forests, shambas, cloud gardens are traditional integrated gardens based on the synergistic growth of a wide variety of plants that produce food, fiber, medicines, teas and other materials for the subsistence farmer. These and other local integrations are an ancient form of permaculture based on the presence and cultivation of several tree species which provide shade support and shelter for numerous lesser food plants as well as fruit, fiber, building material, medicine, edible oil and teas for the farmer.

The advantages of the shamba type integration are many: Shamba type integrations are reservoirs of useful ecotypical cultivars and "poor people's crops" that have great potential value and should be investigated as these plants may be useful in other formats. Shamba type plantings produce a great variety of useful material in very small areas.

Inputs are exclusively local, local knowledge and skill creates and maintains this format which is essentially a managed mini ecosystem. Machinery is not needed. The total harvest index is very high, there is little waste, no run off and the shamba is very resistant to weather events because of its structure and to disease because of its inherent diversity. The plants are domesticated or semi domesticated with some selection for characteristics relating to quality or yield. (See Figure 5 on page 222.)

The disadvantages: Total harvest index is high but the production of products with trade value is not. Most of the food and other products will be used by the shamba farmer. This kind of agriculture is not generally appreciated by western trained scientists. Consequently little research is being done on the plants in the integrations. Many shamba systems are being swallowed up by development or forced out into more marginal areas by conventional agriculture

The one happy exception to this puzzling neglect are the modern permaculturalists who have adopted, modernized, and diversified shamba farming and teach it as part of their discipline.

Hedgerows

In a hedgerow format plants are planted as a boundary, windbreak or a living fence. Many hedgerow plants are minor fruits such as the hawthorn, the bramble, or the myrtle or thorny plants such as the prickly pear, the mesquite or the Kei apple. Wind-breaking trees such as poplar, yew, cypress—larch, neem, tamarisk, and casuarina are also planted in this format.

Advantages: It is not possible to exaggerate how important hedgerows and windbreaking trees are to the health of land used for agriculture. Besides the physical protection the hedgerows provide from drying and eroding winds and the force of other weather events; the hedgerow or windbreak is a refuge for pollinating insects, song—birds and small animals and a storage area for soil moisture. Hedgerows also serve as a preserve for soil organisms destroyed by tilling. Windbreaks and hedgerows may also provide food in the form of fruits, buds, nuts or sap, fencing material, firewood, mulch, edible flowers or teas.

Disadvantages: Much of the useful material from hedgerows is eaten by wildlife and insects—this is only a disadvantage if the farmer is competing for the produce Hedgerows are difficult to harvest and must be kept in control by seasonal pruning. However an agricultural landscape without hedgerows and rows of wind—breaking trees is a vulnerable landscape and sometimes a disaster in the making.

The destruction of windbreaks in Midwestern US was one of the causes of the notorious "dustbowl" of the 1930's.

The loss of thousands of kilometers of hedgerows in England in the last century is the reason for the decline of songbirds and pollinating insects in that country.

Pocket orchards, gum gardens: Pocket orchards and gum garden are integrated temporally as well as spatially as the climax phase of a very long cycle of crop rotation.

For an example, in the traditional systems of rainfed agriculture in the sub—Saharan areas continuous cropping would be followed by a fallow period in which Acacia trees would be allowed to invade the areas. These trees would grow to maturity, protect the soil from erosion and help restructure it—and be tapped for gum for many years. When felled and burned the ashes of the trees enrich the soil for the next cycle of cropping. A similar system exists in the Indian states of Rajasthan, Gujarat and Haryana involving the cultivation of Prosopis cineraria.

In a typical pocket orchard around the Mediterranean olive, scrub oak or other trees with low water requirements are allowed to spread over pasture and garden land to provide shade and forage for livestock. Dry leaves and manure are trodden into the soil for a decade. The trees may be thinned at maturity to form a more permanent copse (small grove or planting) or lopped and burned to promote soil fertility. The trees products may be used by the farmer or fed to livestock.

A similar system was practiced in northerly regions of Europe involving chestnuts, oaks and beech trees with herds of pigs benefiting from the "mast."

Advantages: These formats promote low cost, low input land reclamation for areas with thin, poor soil and encourage locally appropriate use of indigenous trees in a manner that restructures soil and supplies food for livestock.

Disadvantages: this kind of integration is losing ground to "development" of pastoral areas and intensive agriculture.

Nurse tree integrations: Strong quick growing trees, often pioneer plants are planted to shade and protect smaller slow growing species. The weaker species is usually the primary crop but the nurse tree is usually a productive or medicinal plant as well.

Example: Coffee trees nursed by Inga Verra (ice cream bean or pakay) which provide shade and wind protection for the coffee plants.

The advantages are protection and shade for the primary crop, additional produce and material from the nurse crop, and mitigation of difficult cultivation conditions by the swift development of the nurse trees. Nurse tree integrations are suitable for the reclamation of eroding sloping land as well as areas with harsh climates.

Disadvantages: The nature of nurse tree integrations crops impede the use of machinery.

Their close planting formats, slopes, terraces and deliberate mixing of the primary crop and nurse crop demand hand labor and hand harvesting and the use of light agricultural implements.

Agroforestry: Agroforestry formats are usually composed of selected species planted for regenerative purposes in areas denuded by logging, fires, floods and unwise agricultural practices. Agroforestry integrations are also suitable for reclaiming arid and saline lands.

Because of species diversity agoforestry integrations are more easily populated with birds animals and insects than monocultural forestry plantings. For the same reason agroforestry integrations are more resistant to drought and other weather events. There is often an attempt to supply some of the food needs of local populations in addition to supplying firewood, browse and building material.

Harvesting is often complicated due to the extensive nature of such plantings. Skilled labor is required for both management and planting. This is not particularly a disadvantage as many areas where agroforestry is practiced have seriously underemployed populations.

Conventional Orchards and Plantations

Trees are planted at specific intervals and rows are a uniform distance apart. Many orchards are monocultures though some are planted with varieties of the same family of plants or integrated with cover crops. (See Figure 4 on page 221.)

Conventional orchards are usually easy to work by machine and often machinery exists for picking and handling the produce. (See Figure 6 on page 222.)

While conventional orchards and plantations are a high yield format and produce fruits and nuts of more uniform size, tastes and shapes, the ecological and labor costs and correspondingly dear.

Too often commercial plantations are too large for proper stewardship, vulnerable to disease because of uniformity of germplasm and dependent on expensive off farm inputs such as chemical fertilizers, pesticides and herbicides.

Crops in this format are often as "developed" as it is possible to be as units of production—often to the detriment of plant health and the local ecology.

This should not be considered the ultimate target of the domestication process as many conventional orchards and plantations are neither sustainable nor environmentally friendly.

Chapter Three
Evaluating IFT species

Do IFT species need to be improved?

IFT species are in use and usable NOW. They are providing fruits, vegetables, forage, nuts, spices, building, material medicines and dozens of other necessities for some of the world's poorest people.

They are vital resources in much of the developing world.

In some cases *"improving a local resource"* puts it out of reach of local people.

In other cases changing the character of an IFT species might be unnecessary, a case of *"gilding the lily."*

Does an IFT species have to be improved?

Some of them are probably at the peak of their usefulness now.

Others can be made more useful with a little time and effort invested in their selection and breeding.

The first question one must ask when deciding is: what will be lost and what will be gained in the process.

If a species should be improved the next question that must be asked is "how"?

IFT Improvement as a Source of Food
- Nutritive value
- Abundance
- Fruit quality
- Harvest index

Nutritive Value: It may be possible or desirable to improve an IFT species as a source of food. Since some IFT species are more nutritious than domesticated cultivars it might be a case of preserving the existing nutritive value during the domestication process than increasing it. Also there are other factors and characteristics that affect the harvest index of food plants that will have to be addressed sometime during the domestication process such as palatability, flesh to seed ratios, and thickness of peel.

Still many IFT species can be developed as better food sources simply by selecting the most nourishing and palatable of available wild genotypes.

Abundance: There is usually room for improvement as to overall useful yield. A few IFT species are naturally copious bearers such as the marula (Sclerocarya caffra), the zisiphus, and the North American persimmon. These copious bearers can be planted in a manner that will spread out the bearing period for a steady and more manageable supply of fruit.

Modest bearers can often be made more abundant by hybridization and selective breeding.

Alternate bearing species (species which produce a bountiful crop one year and a diminished one the next) may only need a more managed and organized planting methods to become more useful in agricultural formats.

Quality: Almost all IFT species can be improved as to quality. Many characteristics can be manipulated by simple selection including size, color, taste and keeping qualities—all of which contribute to the value of the IFT species as food plants. During this process it is important for the farmer and breeder to keep in mind the developmental targets set for each species. These targets will be determined by the uses, destinations and markets envisioned for the IFT products.

Availability: IFT species with short productive seasons can be made more available by searching out trees which bear earlier or later than most of the species and propagating these trees to extend the season. Introduction of IFT species to an area slightly higher or lower in altitude may extend the fruiting season by several weeks. Introduction to entirely different areas and climates may also extend or stagger bearing times—but the trees will be exposed to many other changes as well.

Better methods of harvesting transport and storage will quickly make IFT fruits more useful as food sources. Much IFT arrives in the household or local marketplace under ripe or overripe, damaged by wildlife or bruised by poor transport and storage.

Improvement as a Crop

1. Hardiness
2. Insect and disease resistance
3. Cold/heat/salt tolerance
4. Seasonality

IFT species have the double advantage of being well adapted to the areas in which they are found and resistant to local challenges such as weather, pests and parasites.

These species start their domestication process with advantages that no imported tree can match. Their general hardiness, their basic tolerances and resistances are intact and protecting the species without help or interference from humanity. These tremendous advantages must be preserved during any attempt at IFT improvement.

This is best done by preserving diversity in initial IFT plantings. To propagate the single best tree in a misguided effort to create an orchard monoculture is simply to remake the mistakes that has led modern agriculture into the blind alley of increasing pesticide use.

The individual resistance of a superior tree is only useful if there is a diverse population of trees in an orchard.

It makes much more sense to propagate the best **dozen** or so of the superior trees and make insect infestation difficult.

IFT species are naturally very hardy and domesticated IFT species will remain so if we do not ignore or misuse this basic strength.

There is however enormous room for improvement in the seasonality of IFT species and whether by careful planting and management or by careful selection from wild types the flowering and bearing periods of IFT species can be manipulated to ensure better utilization of the fruit.

Improvement of integration of the plant into the agricultural system

1. As a source of food for humans
2. As a shade or nurse plant
3. As a hedgerow boundary or margin plant
4. As a host for organisms beneficial to the farm
5. As a source of food for animals
6. As a source of fiber, building material or other useful substances.

There is also much room for improvement as to IFT species integration into agricultural systems.

IFT species should be evaluated not only as sources of food for people but as to the other roles and function they might fulfill.

IFT species' physical characteristics should be taken into account and the species considered as possible nurse trees, shade trees, windbreakers and hedgerow plants.

Also IFT species should be evaluated relative to their abilities to host useful organisms beneficial to the farm or of economic value (for example the mopane tree which is the host to an edible species of caterpillar or the mulberry tree which is the food source of the silkworm).

IFT species should be evaluated as forage plants, sources of fiber or other building materials.

IFT species should be considered as sources of medicines, spices or rare substances as well.

Improvement of integration into the ecosystem

- As a regenerative plant
- As a plant cultivated with local inputs
- As a crop which is resource thrifty
- As a host for beneficial organisms
- As food for wildlife

It is possible to integrate IFT species as crops into local ecosystems for the purpose of reclamation and reforestation. Since the plants are already adapted to the area and conditions there is little chance of failure or ecological disruption.

The fact that the plant is indigenous and extant points to a possible cultivation format that will be both resource—thrifty and based on local inputs. Beneficial organisms and wildlife will already have been exposed to the species and modest increases in the population of the species will most likely have little negative impact.

Improve IFT integration into the economy.
1. For domestic use
2. For trade and barter
3. For the local market
4. As a source of small scale industry
5. As a source of material for VAP
6. For the regional market
7. As a cash crop.

Integrating IFT species for domestic use, trade and barter and the local market should be an immediate priority as this will immediately increase and diversify the food supply for many of the world's poorest citizens.

Next IFT species should be investigated as raw material for small—scale industry and VAP as so many people in the developing world are unemployed.

Some IFT products will reach the regional or global market and some IFT species will become conventional crops but that does not necessarily mean that they are more "valuable" if they do.

They are most valuable where the greatest good is derived for the greatest number of people with a minimum of ecological disruption.

Improve IFT integration into the information base
1. As a wild plant
2. As a cultivar
3. As a regenerative or reclamative plant
4. In a polyculture
5. As food for birds animals and other creatures

6. As a source of usable material
7. As an introduced species in other location
8. As to role in culture religion and mythology

Improving IFT species integration into the agricultural and scientific information base is a necessity if the species are to be domesticated or utilized wisely.

IFT species should be investigated in their wild state, researched in their role as local cultivars and as local regenerative and reclamative plants and the information put in the public domain to increase the choice of usable plants for farmers and foresters.

The value and potential of IFT species as to sources of usable material, rare substances and teas or medicines should also be made known.

The roles of IFT in polycultures, as hosts for insects and birds and as sources of food for wildlife are of great importance in the study of areas where the species are found.

This documentation will greatly help researchers, ecologists and conservationists.

Some IFT species play an important role in regional culture, religion and mythology. For example the etrog or citron is important to the religious life of Jewish people and the indaba tree is important in the culture and mythology of the SADAC region of Africa.

Many IFT species appear in local folklore and folk medicine. This is also valuable information.

Some tools and methods by which the IFT species may be improved as a crop candidate.

One of the first steps in IFT development is the *protection of wild germplasm in situ*. Much can be learned from observing the plant in the plant's native range about the plants requirements, ranges of soil and temperature, yields, life cycle and potential pests and parasites.

Selection from this diverse population of individuals is a next logical step—*trees with valuable or interesting characteristics should be collected from among the wild populations.*

Then proper cultivation, watering and nourishment of the chosen genotypes will allow for a clearer idea of the IFT species potential.

Selection, hybridization and breeding may be the next logical step. Though for many IFT species this work has already been started. Dooryard trees and included trees have already been selected by indigenous farmers and gardeners for characteristic and performance. A high percentage of superior individual trees can be obtained just by taking cuttings from this semi—domesticated germplasm resource.

Grafting may allow a species to survive in a new soil type or an adverse environment.

Vegetative propagation of superior individuals trees will lead to the creation of the varieties that will be needed to plant groves and orchards. Multiple diverse varieties should be established in this initial stage of domestication to avoid losing valuable genetic material by too severe and early selection.

Continued gene flow from wild relatives and populations will prevent inbreeding depression and allow for continuing evolution.

The sequence of events which would lead to an IFT species being integrated into an agricultural system might theoretically proceed in this direction and manner:

1. Study and collection of wild germplasm preserved

   in situ
2. Establishment of genotype collection
3. Establishment of nursery for the IFT species
4. Introduction orchards
5. Out planting and extension to local farmers
6. Distribution of saplings for small domestic plant-ings
7. Distribution of saplings for polyculture
8. Deliberate introduction to areas in need of regen-erative strategies
9. Introduction in other areas or locales
10. Establishment of commercial orchards

This is theoretical sequence or domestication path-way only as few IFT species will become commercial cultivars.

There are also many different pathways to domesti-cation, some accompanied by research and develop-ment protocols and some quite spontaneous and specific to area.

Most IFT species will find their optimal use and inte-gration in states preceding commercial orchardry.

Chapter Four
Evaluating Specific Species

Against what standard should the IFT species and the IFT product be measured?

How can it be known if a species should be left in situ as a local resource—or domesticated and moved along one of the developmental pathways?

How can it be known if the IFT species has global potential as a food producer or the potential to be a vital regenerative plant or reclamative outside of its native range?

It is best to start with the potential of the species within the native range and to look closely at its uses, problems, and properties.

The farmer or researcher can evaluate most species by using a simple questionnaire.

IFT Evaluation

1. Are the fruits good enough for the local market?
   - Size
   - Taste
   - Keeping qualities
   - Quantity
   - Other possible problems (fibers, leaching, blanching)

2. Can a modest program of breeding and selection add to their usefulness?
   - Improve the size
   - Improve the taste
   - Improve other qualities
   - Increase the quantity of the products

- Extend the range in which the tree can be plantcd
- Improve disease resistance
- Improve hardiness and tolerances
- Improve the worth of the products in cash or barter

3. Can a modest VAP program boost development?
   - Give the fruit more value on the local market
   - Make the use of the fruit or the products more widespread.
   - Spark commercial interest or R and D
   - Encourage the planting of trees in small domestic formats
   - Add an important dietary element to the local range of available foods
   - Extend the period of time the fruit or the product is available
   - Provide additional income to the existing collectors/growers of the fruit.

Until this point the evaluation process has dealt with the IFT species vis a vis the local environment and economy.

The versatility, yield, hardiness and malleability of the species are the deciding factor in development beyond local needs and markets:

4. Can the IFT species be introduced to other areas?
   - As a fresh fruit or VAP product
   - As a tree in domestic formats
   - As a regenerating or reforesting tree
   - As part of an arboreal integration
   - For a test or introduction planting
   - For other purposes such as windbreaks or living fences
   - For secondary products and uses such as animal feed, oil, building or craft materials

- To provide food during a hungry season or improve the local diet.

5. Should the IFT species be planted in commercial formats?
   - In an Non Timber Forest Product or Non Timber Tree Product integration
   - For secondary uses or purposes (such as a nurse tree or host tree)
   - Small orchards or local commerce
   - Plantation format inside the country of origin
   - Possible cash crop or export crop

6. Where does the IFT product/fruit have more value?
   - As a local food product for domestic consumption
   - Exclusive regional sale (local specialty)
   - NWFP (Non Wood Forest Product) green (ecological) market
   - Plantation for domestic use
   - Export and cash markets
   - Use in making VAP

7. Where does the tree have more value?
   - In small domestic formats
   - As part of an integration
   - As a regenerative plant
   - As a windbreak, hedgerow or boundary tree
   - Ecotypical cultivar
   - As a commercial cultivar

8. What sort of Research and Development (R and D) is needed?
   - Basic research
   - Ecological role in native range
   - R and D for improvement of fruit and plant
   - " " for improved domestic use
   - " " as to specific pests, disease and problems
   - " " for use a raw material
   - " " as to use in integrations

- " " as to use as a regenerative
- " " as to secondary uses
- " " as to range of VAP products
- " " with an eye to commercial planting
- R and D with an eye to marketing.

In short—What is the developmental target??

It is also important to remember that IFT species may be appropriate in many formats.

Development along one pathway does not preclude progress along another.

An IFT species may be developed in several directions. The versatile marula tree for example may be developed for making liquor by selecting and propagating high sugar types **and** developed for table fruit by selecting and propagating trees with especially large fruits.

The hardy, spiny drought tolerant Balanites aegypticus or lalob may be developed as a source of materia medica **and** as a fodder producing tree.

The huge baobab is esteemed for its fiberous bark used to make rope, its large fruits that weigh several pounds and can be eaten or used to make soft drinks, its edible leaves and flowers and its ability to withstand drought. Holistically this tree is suitable for land reclamation **and** wildcrafting **and** local integrations

A large, beautiful and hardy IFT species like the Jackalberry (Diospyros mespiliformis) may be developed for fruit production **and** as an ornamental plant or wind breaker tree.

Chapter Five
Where do we start/Where are we going?

There are over 15,000 edible, medicinal or useful products that come from perennial plants that have **NOT BEEN DOMESTICATED.**

The task of domesticating even a few of them seems impossibly hard

Where do we start?

Begin with Local Food Plants

Obviously we should begin with IFT fruit and food crops of local importance—they are half—way on the road to domestication since they are known and used by local people.

Sometimes the plants life cycle has already been documented, pests or diseases observed, and knowledge of planting or grafting techniques acquired by local gardeners.

Therefore local food plants are a rich source of possible crop candidates.

Advantages at this level of domestication:

1. The species is already in use
2. Local people know its value
3. There is material for propagation and experimentation
4. There may already be a small ready—made market
5. There may be a body of local knowledge about the plant
6. There is probably considerable variation in the

local population of the IFT species

Dooryard Trees and Farmyard Trees

Dooryard and farmyard trees and other included germplasm are another population of plants full of promise.

Superior individuals and types may been identified in such populations, knowledge of the life cycle of the plant and needs of the plant can be acquired from local farmers and gardeners. This makes the work of the agronomist much easier and the pathway to domestication a short one.

There is still considerable variation in the plant populations of dooryard and farmyard trees but some selection has already taken place—usually because of the valuable characteristics of the primary product.

Advantages at this level of domestication:

1. The domestication process has already started
2. Local people know how to plant and cultivate the species
3. Considerable genetic resources remain in local wilderness
4. The plant has proved useful to the economy of the farm or household.
5. Local people may know how to make VAP
6. Local people may have found other uses or properties in the species

IFT Species in parks, woodlands

IFT plants in parks, woodlands and integrations are also IFT populations with great potential because local people are knowledgeable about the plants use and habitat—while in—species diversity is for the most part intact.

Knowledge about the IFT species from the caretakers of these areas may point to uses and attributes of the plant that the researcher may not be aware of or give the scientist bent on domestication an idea as to where these species might be introduced as crop candidates.

Often local knowledge will include data about plant to plant and plant to animal interaction. At this level it is also possible to glean much information about pollinators, vectors, plant parasites and plant life cycles.

The advantage at this level of domestication:

1. Many plants have known valuable attributes, products, effects
2. Some R and D by conservationists, forest service
3. Benefit to local ecology and wild life known
4. May be attractive to green (ecological) markets
5. Enough IFT product or material may be available to enter or create a market

Wild IFT

The pathway to domestication with wild IFT may be long, especially if the species is only accessible to wildcrafters or is found only in remote or hostile environments.

Still there are some advantages to complete wildness:

1. A unique or new product may be discovered in wild and unknown IFT
2. Responsibly wildcrafted materials may be attractive to green markets
3. The species most likely possesses intact variability, adaptability and disease resistance
4. The species may have domesticated or semi domesticated relatives which can be improved by interbreeding with the wild plant—or the wild

plant may provide a rootstock or other necessary plant matcrial for improvement of domesticated relatives.

5. The species may be the focus of ecological research or R and D not connected with the IFT as a product
6. A unique body of ethno—botanical information may be acquired along with the plant.

In this case a brief set of questions helps the farmer or researcher evaluate the possibilities....

There are also many different pathways to domestication, some accompanied by research and development protocols and some quite spontaneous and specific to area.

Semi—domesticated plant material

1. What is the total value to the local economy?
2. Harvest index: how many useful products? How many uses?
3. Is the IFT product bought from small farmers and householders, gathered from common land?
4. Is the IFT product a regional specialty or does the IFT product have potential to enter other markets?
5. Supply, packing, transport: how does the product get to market?
6. VAP—is anyone making jam, wine, crafted goods, dried fruits etc from the IFT?

Plants from integrated agriculture

1. Quantity and quality concerns—how much product in what condition?
2. Collection, packing and transport——how to get it to market?
3. Interaction and ecological value—how does harvesting the product influence the rest of the integration?

4. Green and ecological market concerns—is utilization endangering the resource?
5. Tenure and conservation—who has the right to pick, gather, sell, use the product?

Wild Germplasm

1. Are the products present in local markets?
2. How much of the IFT product is available?
3. What is the quality of the IFT product?
4. Seasonality—available when? For how long a season?
5. Shelf life/Perishability
6. Effect on the IFT resource base—is the product being harvested sustainably?
7. Will the wild IFT product be attractive the green market? Other markets?

Answering these questions leads to decision making an many pathways and possibilities

Possibilities for semi-domesticated germplasm

1. Leave in situ
2. Utilize more fully in the local markets
3. Bring to other areas and markets
4. Utilize in other formats
5. Investigate as a regenerative plant
6. Promote VAP with an eye to small scale industry
7. Attempt full domestication

Possibilities for germplasm that is domesticated but not commercialized

1. Extend markets
2. Investigate VAP
3. Investigate as a potential regenerative agricultural element
4. Enter into plantation formats
5. Cultivate with conventional agricultural parameters

6. Cultivate for the organic or green market

Possibilities for wild germplasm

1. Leave in situ
2. Leave in situ and attempt conservation
3. Leave in situ, utilize in an ecologically sound manner
4. Leave in wild, utilize ecologically. Conserve as a gene bank
5. Extract some germplasm for domestication and experimentation
6. Extract germplasm for experimentation while conserving original plants and stands
7. Introduce or use to enrich integrations
8. Land reclamation, agroforestry, possibilities in native range

At some point in the domestication process of IFT the farmer or researcher must decide what the developmental targets are and how best to bring the IFT species to that level of development.

Clearly much IFT cannot travel the entire route to the orchard, plantation and global market.

The IFT product might not be suitable for commercialization for any number of reasons.

Some IFT products have a short shelf life or appeal to a limited group of people as food.

Some IFT species have multiple products and uses and much of their potential would be wasted in a plantation or an orchard format.

Other IFT species have such a powerful influence on the local ecology that they should be planted in integration or land reclamation projects where they can serve as protective barriers, apiary plants, nurse trees and companion plants—as well as produce their primary products.

That does not mean this germplasm is inferior or unworthy of development—just that this particular species is more suitable to a different format with a holistic rather than commercial intent.

IFT species unsuitable for commercial formats should not be regarded as "second class"—they are just as potentially important for local economies and probably more important for local ecology than the trees that can be relegated to orchards, plantations and conventional developmental pathways.

What then should be the developmental targets of a program to domesticate IFT?

Possible Developmental Targets

1. Ecologically and Socially Friendly Utilization As A Wild Crop

Explanation: In this format the plants are preserved in situ and collected for sale or use by local people who are licensed, sanctioned or allowed to hold stewardship over the wild crop.

Examples of stewards and users of the wild IFT species are extractivists of non—timber forest products, tappers of wild rubber, "organic leather collectors, honey hunters, collectors of rainforest drugs, xiji (a xiji is an agreed upon territory usually wild crafted by one family where frankincense trees(Boswellia sacra) grow naturally) harvesters of frankincense.

The local benefits of such formats are: food, useful material and employment. Other benefits include continued local use of the crop, protection of land from uncontrolled exploitation, protection of wild crop from theft, extinction and gene piracy, as well small cash and niche products for gatherers.

What is needed for this kind of protection and use?

Most needed is government recognition that the wild crop has worth AS a wild crop, cooperation and coordination among NGOs researching wild crops, and measures to preserve centers of wild crop diversity and the existing population of plants.

Also important to this developmental target is legislation to protect the rights of local people to the use of the wild crop and the monetary benefits derived from the wild crop.

Research into wildlife and ecology of the wildcrafted area would also be helpful

As would be expanded information pathways between researchers, scientists, government representatives, and local people.

Conserving and ecological methods of harvesting transporting and packing the wild crop are also necessary for proper utilization of wildcrafted material.

Research of the role of the wild crop in the local ecosystem and the regenerative capacity of the wild crop are crucial if the wildcrop is not to be overexploited.

2. Local Ecotypical Cultivar

Explanation: The IFT species becomes a local crop adapted to the seasonality, weather soil and water resources of a specific locale. Most of the plant material is used or consumed by the farmers or sold in the local market. Some produce may be traded or turned into VAP. Little money and effort is invested in transporting, packaging or advertisement therefore a high percentage of the crop's direct value enters the local economy.

Examples of this kind of use: Harvested and utilized in this manner are the following products: Asian leaf vegetables, Andean potatoes, ancient grains such as tef, african red rice, karamaka, fonio or amaranth as well as tree crops such as the capuli, the naranjilla, the goldenberry, the lucuma.

Local benefits: The local area and ecology gains resource appropriate cultivars for the farm, food for the farm household, and the utilization of agricultural waste as animal feed or compost. Local benefits also include affordable and appropriate fresh foods for the community, local employment, some sale or trade value and basis for cottage industry.

What is needed to encourage or establish such patterns of use?

Needed most is government recognition of the value of local eco—cultivars, and co—ordination between NGOs working to restore local cropping systems Journals, newsletters, websites to disseminate and exchange information, and research in cultivar improvement would be helpful as well as placement of local cultivars in seed banks and working collections of plant breeders. Protection from "globalization" is necessary to preserve cultivars and the landraces from which they were derived. Microcredit loans for the planting of ecotypical cultivars and the creation of cottage industry would be helpful. Research into storage, processing and possible VAP would allow the participants in these projects to profit financially from their labors.

3. Integrated Crop

Explanation: The IFT species are an element in traditional permaculture planting such as shambas, forest gardens, cloud gardens supplying support, nourishment, protection and shade as well as useful or edible products.

Example of IFT species in such a format: The basul bean tree of South America that supplies shade to gardens and other trees. Other trees planted as the "top story" of permacultural integrations are the pacay tree, the rubber tree, the damar tree, the tamarind, the date palm, the cinnamon tree, and the mulberry. All can be planted to shade and shelter an integrated agricultural system with smaller trees, bushes, herbs and vegetables as the sheltered "lower storey" crops.

Local benefits of these integrations include food and useable material for immediate consumption, employment and some trade products. Other benefits include, preservation of land in traditional usage patterns, fodder for domestic animals, and habitat for insects and wildlife. These gardens also attract pollinators and predatory insects, bolster anti erosion strategies, and provide genetic reservoirs of plant germplasm.

What is needed to establish or protect integrated gardens?

Firstly recognition of the value of traditional and new permacultural and silvicultural systems is necessary plus, aid from NGOs and governments in preserving and establishing such systems in appropriate areas. Tenure for silviculturalists is needed as well as ecological methods of gathering, transport and post harvest of the products. Research into wildlife concerns, and polycultural balances would be helpful as well as the establishment of information pathways at all levels.

4. Agroforestry strategies

Explanation: The trees are planted purposely to regenerate denuded, burned, overgrazed or depleted areas with an eye to sustainable production of tree products. Native species are often the basis of the plantings though some successful planting use introduced trees. Agroforestry projects are being carried out in many countries and almost every climatic zone and there is an immense variation in regard to species, format, and patterns of planting introduction, and reintroduction.

Examples of agroforestry formats: Wild rubber trees are reintroduced and interplanted with nut trees in logged over areas of the Amazon. Lalob, zisiphus, acacia and terebinths have been reintroduced to Israel's arid south. The replanting of oaks and conifers has been successful on burned slopes in California. ICRAF (International Center for Research in Agroforestry) projects with trees that produce non wood forest products in tropical Africa are good examples of modern agroforestry as well, the establishment of *"gum and butter"* parks in more arid areas.

Local benefits: Agroforestry formats generate local employment and boost local food opportunities. Agroforestry may supply inputs and habitats for animal husbandry and refuge for wildlife. Firewood and building material as well as other forest products may find their way into local markets. Agroforestry and other such systems create employment for extractivists and wildcrafters.

What is needed to encourage the creation and protection of agroforestry formats?

It will be necessary to grant tenure for local residents and strike a balance between agroforestry and further development. Restrained repopulation of reforested areas will protect these areas rather than deplete them. Cooperation between governments and NGOs and extractivist organizations will allow for the reforestation of other desolate areas. Greater coordination with green consumers and green markets will encourage research into long term sustainability and economics as well as research into ecological balances within projects.

5. Small Domesticated Formats.

These formats include pocket orchards, yard trees common copses, integrated arboreal rotations which are all basically local features of the landscape and often planted and maintained on common land.

Examples of this format are gum gardens, berry slopes, and tree commons.

Local benefits: Local nourishment and employment is the primary benefit, but these groves also provide shade and wind protection, aesthetic enhancement around dwellings and high vitamin food for hungry seasons. There are some VAP possibilities and trade value at this level of domestication. Some IFT products are used as animal feed. But species in this format constitute a reservoir of semi domesticated plant germplasm with a high percentage of superior individuals and much detailed information on use and cultivation of the germplasm can be gleaned from these small formats.

What is needed to promote IFT use in these formats?

Obviously recognition of the worth and food value of small domesticated formats, and microcredit loans for introducing small plantings to poor communities would be the first step. The propagation and distribution of suitable trees, and education as to use, possibilities and cultivation of the IFT species should follow. Cooperation on a local level as to marketing and cottage industry and low tech information pathways such as newsletters in local languages or newspaper articles in local papers would promote the proper utilization of the germplasm. Cooperation between local and national authorities and more help from NGO's would be very helpful in protecting these groves.

6. Margins

Explanations Trees, bushes, plants, cane fruits and vines are planted as living fences, hedgerows, windbreaks and boundaries. The primary reason for these planting is not food production but the protection of land or crops from wind, sun, or animals water storage in the soil and benefits to wildlife. The chosen species usually have a use or value beyond their structural one and produce minor fruits, spices, building material or medicinal material.

Examples of some plants used in margins are briars, hawthorn, prickly pear cactus, kei apple, yew, bamboos, birch, poplars, cedars, and cypress larch.

Many plants have been used as margin or boundary plants including grasses and domesticated fruit trees.

Local benefits: The most visible benefits are the resulting living fences and windbreaks that ensure a measure of privacy, and add aesthetic value to the landscape Planted margins also absorb dust and noise and protect the soil from erosion as well as providing a refuge for songbirds, pollinating insects and predatory insects.

Some IFT species used in margins have considerable usefulness in animal husbandry and as high vitamin food, or produce minor food products such as currants, berries, haws, herbal tea.

What is needed to promote this format?

Ecologically sound margin planting is unfortunately in decline with a great loss in the latter half of the 20th century of hedgerows, windbreaks and copses. Recognition of the value of margins in relation to songbird and pollinator populations and overall ecological balance (especially in developed countries) is a necessity if intelligent margin planting is to return.

Protected margins are very important to agricultural well-being in conventionally cultivated areas. Also crucial to margin return is legislation and zoning protecting existing margins and farmland, reintroduction of planted margins as buffer zones between agricultural areas and dwellings, and education as to benefits of margins in relation to cultivated crops and ecological health. More interest and R and D by NGO's as well as information pathways at local levels could be helpful.

IFT species suitable to any of these formats are more likely to be utilized holistically and not developed solely for the use of their primary product.

Chapter Six
Towards a Second Domestication

Most of the food plants the human race depends on were domesticated long ago. Agronomists and agricultural specialists agree that modern humans have domesticated few new food plants. Indeed, some reputable authorities contend that modern man has domesticated **NO** new food plants.

This would not be a critical issue if we were capable of preserving and protecting the rich agricultural heritage left to us by our ancestors. Unfortunately slightly over a hundred years ago science and business took over farming and the entire process of food production stopped looking like agriculture and started to look like manufacturing.

The logic of the assembly line and the shoe factory was misapplied mercilessly to the farm.

The result was a gross oversimplification of culture and endeavor that has left farming impoverished in relation to the genetic diversity of crops and within crops, vulnerable to pests, unsustainable in relation to soil and water use and ruinous to the rural community.

In other words, each time the agricultural wheel was reinvented in the last century more crops and more varieties of crops were discarded, the use of crop protective chemicals produced more resistance in more pests, more artificial fertilizers were given in the form of destructive chemical salts and more farmers were replaced by machines.

In each version of agriculture more people were left outside the circle, to be forced off their land and into cities where no jobs wait for them or left to be poor and hungry on lands that once supported their parents and grandparents as "progress" passed them by.

In each new version of agriculture less attention was paid to the health of the soil, the water and the organisms and the local traditions that make farming possible.

Now at the beginning of the 21st century all the living breathing elements of the modern agricultural system are in poor shape: crop plants are genetically impoverished and static, animals are saturated with antibiotics and hormones and forced to produce milk, meat or eggs beyond their natural capacity, farmers are bankrupt and have been driven off the land by the millions, agricultural land and water have been dangerously degraded.... and the consumers of the first world, the recipients of the bounty of this monstrous horn of plenty are sick, obese, cancer prone and unhappy—while a good deal of the rest of the world is chronically hungry.

It should be obvious to most people that applying the principals and methods of the factory to our food systems was a serious mistake.

Good food cannot be made like plastic sandals.

The entire point of farming is to produce good food to support human life on earth,—a basic truth eclipsed by a skewed system of values that puts a great deal of value on what can be measured by the pound and sold, but little on less tangible things like community, happiness or health.

Good agriculture can only done by tapping into the bounty of the natural world in an organized intelligent manner that does not destroy the resource base upon which we depend.

Natural eco—systems are complex, self regulating, self—sustaining and very diverse.

These systems are not only the ultimate source of all the plants, creatures and genes we use in agriculture—they should be the templates of our agricultural endeavors as well.

Now is the time to defy conventional wisdom and make farming systems more complex and more diverse, to bring in new crops with new qualities, fresh resistances, new economic opportunities, new ways to help the hungry feed themselves.

Good agriculture can only be done by people who know how to farm. We need more hands and heads in agriculture not fewer. We need people who know how to farm well, who love their homes and are rooted in local culture and tradition, who can work to feed their fellow citizens without spoiling the earth.

When one looks at the oversimplified, vulnerable, chemical—soaked farms, denied adequate human resources: and the masses of unemployed citizens in the cities, denied the chance to make a living it seems there must be a way to put the two problems together to make a solution....

Now when we redraw the circle we should include the landless, the jobless, the traditional farmers, the unrecognized untenured wild crafters, rubber tappers, spice gatherers, native healers.

We need their skills, their wisdom, their patience and their local knowledge.

We need the tools, methods and energy of modern R and D as well.

We must tap into the crop potential of the entire planet and do it in a way that recognizes the beauty, complexity and fragility of our world.

The logic of the shoe factory must be discarded.

Applying the rules of one system to another system that is utterly different is **NOT** progressive or efficient or "modern."

Sometimes it is merely stupid.

Often it is completely destructive.

What is domestication?

If we are to create new crop systems by domesticating and utilizing IFT species perhaps a short explanation of the domestication process would be helpful to the reader. Domestication's four meanings in Websters Dictionary: 1. *to bring into domestic use* 2. *to fit for domestic life* 3. *to adapt to intimate association with and to the advantage of man* 4. *to bring to the level of ordinary people*

When we domesticate a plant we divert a certain amount of a wild population of plants or animals to be our charge, our property and for our use.

Many plants and animals were brought into the continuum of human use over a period of hundreds of thousands of years.

These organisms underwent accelerated and human—induced evolution including the selection and nurture of natural variations for specific characteristics and purposes and genetic changes deliberately induced in populations to make the species more useful to mankind.

To give examples: Wheat has been bred from a simple annual Middle Eastern grass into a mighty family of varieties, types and ecotypes, grown on all inhabited continents. The common dog has been bred from the wolf into toy dogs, hunting dogs guard dogs—over a thousand recognized breeds with incredible variability in size, shape color and temperament.

The Five Steps of Historical Domestication

1. Plants and other organisms are recognized as useful
2. Germplasm is gathered with the intention of establishing a controlled population
3. Accelerated, human induced evolution by selection
4. Selection and nurture of natural variations for specific characteristics and purposes
5. Deliberate breeding to fix characteristics in the controlled population

In other words, the descendent of the wolf became man's companion instead of his enemy; a wild grass from the Middle East became the staff of human life. For good or for ill the humans involved in the domestication process also gave up their wildness and settled in specific areas, or followed the migrations of animals—not as hunters but as herders.

There were certain genetic consequences for the organisms that lost their independence and their wildness. There were both losses and gains of genetic material, modification of gene function, modification of gene complexes, modification of genetic identity.

Genetic Consequences for Domesticated Organisms

1. Loss of genetic material
2. Gain of genetic material
3. Modification of gene function
4. Modification of gene complexes
5. Modification of genetic identity.

The consequences for the domesticators were almost as radical as for the animals and plants. Stone age nomadic cultures changed the vegetations patterns, managed the plant and animal population in a sophisticated manner and increased so steadily in number that it was no longer possible to live solely from natural bounty.

Organized agriculture most likely arose because of conflicts over territory and population pressure on the wild resource base.

With these changes came changes to the natural world and to human societies leading to what we would roughly call civilization.

The first domestication changed human society forever.

What might be expected then, from a second domestication?

Consequences of a Second Domestication
A change of heart?

Not a revolution perhaps but an affirmation of what we all know in our hearts...the earth is our only home and we must find the way to live on it and to make our living from it without bringing it to the brink of destruction.

More food where it is needed.

One of the reasons there is hunger in the world is because there is an increasing number of people who cannot earn enough money to buy food and no longer have the land or resources to grow it themselves.

In the long run these populations cannot be saved by food aid or maintained by global charity. They must be encouraged and allowed to support themselves. Even a modest program to introduce new food crops and domesticate or utilize local wild foods and IFT could significantly alleviate hunger in the countryside of the developing world—exactly the place where hunger is most acute.

Economic opportunities. New crops and crop systems mean new opportunities for farmers, traditional permaculturalists and wild crafters, more small businesses and cottage industries for emerging VAP, perhaps even new industries and processes for products which reach the global market.

Personal health. Such a program would give some people the chance to support themselves while allowing others to taste new foods, new flavors and acquire new sources of nourishment. The twenty overused mega crops of modern agriculture have seriously eroded the variety of foodstuff available— even as the markets of the world are swamped by the products of the overproduction of these crops.

Better global health. Farming systems based on natural principles will halt desertification. Agroforestry, reforestation and no till strategies of land use will improve the carbon cycle and help slow global warming. A return to organic patterns of fertilizer use will allow the ocean's 146 "dead zones" caused by fertilizer run—off to recover.

These hypoxic or oxygen depleted areas have been documented all over the world from the Adriatic to the Yellow Sea and they are the direct results of the overuse and subsequent run—off of nitrogen and phosphorus based fertilizer. Excess nitrogen combined with placid summer weather feed bumper crops of phytoplankton that grow rapidly then drift to the bottom and die. The process of decay requires oxygen and oxygen is depleted in the bottom layers of water. This forces many bottom dwelling species to come to the surface layers of water just to survive and wipes out some species entirely.

New plant based medicines: The investigation of IFT, wild plants, local food plants and medicinal plants in a sane, fair, intelligent and careful manner is much more likely to yield the wonder drugs and medicines of the future than the "gold rush" of current gene prospecting practices. Local people have no reason to cooperate with a system that exploits their knowledge without rewarding or recognizing it. Local farmers and wild crafters have no reason to pass on knowledge to parties who may attempt to hijack local botanical treasures or patent them and prevent further development of these resources within the community. Certainly local traditional permaculturalists have no reason to give up their plants and seeds to corporations that intend to make their way of life impossible.

New plant products: The sustainable collection of gums, oils, fibers, sap and other rare substances will lead to the availability of new products such as "organic leather" a leather substitute made from the sap of a South American tree and harvested in an ecologically sound manner or green Tencel, a fabric made from the sustainable harvesting of bark.

All these changes will allow the new agriculture to reestablish roots in the local economy.

This is a critical step in the reestablishment of reliable local food supplies and local production of salable goods and necessities.

It is also a critical step in the revitalization of the countryside.

In too many places the needs of the local people have been neglected as the best part of land and water resources are dedicated to producing cash crops for the global market.

In too many places agriculture has become mechanized, dependent on expensive imported inputs, cruel to the land and wasteful of local resources.

Cropping systems based on IFT or new crops should be intensely local, integrated into an area as the cloud garden or shamba used to be, providing first food and livelihood for local people.

When local abundance is reestablished goods for the larger markets will also flow more freely.

There is much to be gained and little to be lost by starting the process of domestication for local IFT, indeed in many cases much of the work has already begun. Bringing the IFT species into the continuum of human use will not take hundreds of years but can be done quite quickly.

The very process of domestication, planting and cultivation of IFT species in the hungry areas of the world will bring about a host of immediate benefits from employment opportunities for those who have no work, food for those who suffer from food insecurity and environmental reclamation for those who live in depleted and devastated areas.

IFT derived benefits in the developed world would include the all the previously stated benefits with the addition of noise and pollution mitigation in urban areas, shade and protection from wind in rural areas an ecological regeneration in eroded and depleted areas, some of them "worked out" by unwise conventional agriculture.

For the future of the earth, let us hope that the Second Domestication happens sooner than later.

Chapter Seven
Who Can Help?

IFT species have finally been recognized as vital genetic and economic resources that carry the potential for increasing the food supply for rural people without unduly disrupting the environment.

There are currently many societies, NGOs agencies and academic bodies that are seriously investigating IFT species. Some have already begun the work of evaluation and domestication.

But IFT species will only reach their potential for human use and ecological regeneration of agriculture if the unwise agricultural practices of the last century give way to more enlightened ideas.

IFT species must be recognized as part of the global commons.

They should not be owned, staked out or divided up between interested bodies but developed cooperatively by the people who will use, safeguard and maintain these plants.

To this end germplasm and information should be shared. The people who are developing the marula in Botswana should be the partners—not the rivals—of the people who are working with the tree in Zimbabwe.

The process will be faster, the results will be better, and the markets will be broader if IFT protection and development can be a point of agreement between peoples and not a bone of contention.

Also when the time comes to expand planting or production of a species which can enter the global market there will be more of a chance of raising the needed capital if people, institutions and nations involved can work together.

There are no shortcuts—the domestication of even one species is a daunting task, one that can discourage the most determined researcher.

To illustrate this point consider the initial assessment and the first steps in the domestication of the IFT species.

Initial Asessment/First Steps

1. Identify possible products: fruit, nut, pod, pith, sap, leaves, other
2. Identify the plant, the plant family, the native range
3. Take a census of the plant in the immediate area
4. Does the plant population need protection?
5. Are the plant's products already picked or collected?
6. Seasonality of the plant, when should plant products be harvested?
7. Use of the plant—who or what currently benefits from the fruit/nuts/other products?
8. Do a survey among local people, document local knowledge
9. Investigate folklore and archival material
10. Investigate secondary and tertiary uses of plant products
11. Investigate role in the ecosystem
12. Is this a renewable resource? Can harvesting be done sustainably?
13. Investigate the variability in the local population
14. Do basic research on the wild population
15. Establish a collection of plants/seeds/germplasm
16. Do basic research on the cultivated population.

This is all before any real experiments in agricultural mode such as grafting or vegetative propagation.

Luckily there are pools of knowledge, expertise and funding which can be tapped.

Who can help?

1. **Local people**: farmers, hunters, tappers, wildcrafters, birdwatchers, and local children

These people can often tell an IFT researcher where the best trees are relative to size taste color and quality of product. They may know much about the trees life cycle, which birds, animals and insects are associated with a particular species. They often can supply important information about the seasonality of the product, when and how it is best to gather and store it. They can often tell an IFT researcher of medicinal uses of local plants, recount folklore, help map local populations and associations of plants and define the plants range as to available moisture and optimal altitude. Local farmers are important informants relating to included germplasm and boundary plants and local herdsmen can often access an IFT species value as fodder, forage, a source building material, medicinal substances or as windbreaks.

In short local people are extremely valuable sources of knowledge about IFT species and should be listened to with respect.

2. **Conservationists**: rangers. local botanists, forest guards, game wardens, guides, scouts.

These people are often important sources of information relative to the role of the IFT species in the ecosystem. They may visit plants or plant populations when no fruit is available and so be able to describe dormant periods, flowering, periods of fast growth.

They may know which migratory creatures are associated with the species and have a clear picture of the plants life cycle as well as its holistic value in the landscape.

They also may be able to pinpoint populations of plants in danger because of unsustainable harvesting or over—utilization of a species during a hungry season.

3. **Researchers** from biodiversity surveys, mapping expeditions.

This relatively small group of scientists can be of great assistance during census taking, the mapping of a species native range, determining the location of relict populations or identifying the centers of biodiversity.

4. **Regional organizations**: Councils, seed saver associations, gardening clubs and professional clubs.

Regional organizations should not be overlooked as they often can supply information about local uses of IFT products, local developmental needs and the value of IFT in the marketplace. They also may supply information about desired VAP products, and have useful insights about labor and transport. Regional R and D bodies can often help with seed storage, networking and nursery services

5. **NGOs (Non Governmental Organizations)** and sustainable development organizations.

NGO's, private philanthropic funds and sustainable development organization are important sources of *"seed money"* that is money to get started, equipment and teaching materials. They can facilitate the extension of credit and loans, encourage local participation, foster connections to international bodies and mediate between the local interested parties and governmental bodies and organizations.

6. **Government bodies** dedicated to conservation, forestry land reclamation or management: These bodies can provide information about the environment, supply funding, scientific expertise and supervision. Nursery services and seed banks are often owned or managed by this kind of government body. Enlisting government bodies dedicated to conservation or environmental improvement can lead to protective legislation for IFT species, legislation to impose restriction or grant tenure on IFT use, and backing for restoration ecology efforts.

IFT projects have a much better chance of succeeding with the backing of **both** regional and national governments.

7. **International organizations** such as the FAO, the ICRAF, Oxfam etc.

These organizations can provide the IFT researcher with scientific expertise, funding or information about acquiring funds. International organizations may also extend credit, donate teaching materials, facilitate networking with other researchers, help with the organization of conferences, and give support for newsletters and publications.

One should not hesitate to contact these organizations no matter how humble or local the project. Their publications and websites are packed with useful information and suggestions.

8. **Archives**: Archives can be valuable sources of information relating to past populations, records of former use or cultivation, visual material such as sketches, cultural or mythic associations.

9. **Historical societies, the journals of travelers and explorers**: Historical societies are good sources of early visual material in the form of sketches and photographs. The journals of early explorers often contain sketches and description of plants, plant products and plant populations as well as drawings of the wildlife associated with the plants.

10. **Specialized literature**: Specialized literature such as papers monographs and reports supply data about specific concerns, phenomena or problems associated with IFT species as well as much information about associated plants and animals.

11. **Folklorists**: Folklorists and healers are the primary source of information about the other dimensions and uses of IFT, as well as ritual information, medicinal properties and religious and cultural associations.

12. **Internet sites**: The internet is a source of easily available information of all kinds as well as photographs and contact information for other interested parties. The internet greatly facilitates consultation, information exchange and networking.

IFT researchers should considering contacting all of these parties in the course of their work. There is a well of accumulated knowledge and experience to tap that will greatly aid in the IFT species development or preservation.

The free flow of information and ideas about IFT species and input from interested parties who are not necessarily scientists will help the IFT researcher gain a clear picture of the potential of the species, its holistic value in the community and the landscape and its possible integration in broader environmental projects.

This knowledge is a gift and allows the IFT researcher to start a project or study without having to start from zero. No source, however distant or humble should be overlooked.

Another question the IFT worker or researcher should ask is: **who can I help?**

There is a great need for information relating to IFT species relating to their potential as crops, their value in agroforestry and restoration efforts and their market value. Simple recipes for VAP such as preserves, wines, beer, oils or fruit leather are especially valuable to farmers. How can this information be desseminated? IFT is important most of all to the rural poor who do not commonly have access to the internet, subscribe to newspapers or go to conferences.

Perhaps the relevant information can reach those who need it by newsletter or by lectures at local educational facilities. Information can be translated into local language posted on bulletin boards in local markets and gathering places.

The IFT researcher must ask how he or she can contribute to this effort.

Chapter Eight
Dooryard and Farmyard Trees and Family Feeding Programs

The best way to combat hunger among the rural poor is to increase the amount and diversity of food at the most basic level, ie. the food householders can produce themselves.

This circumvents all the obstacles to food security thrown up by politics, economics and neglect of outlying areas by central governments.

The equation is simple. Householders produce food and value added products. They consume the food and use the products. Any surplus is stored, or used in the extended family. Surplus is also sold or bartered locally.

All these activities also benefit the household.

At this level of use the direct value of IFT species is clearly visible.

Studies in Brazil, Sri Lanka the Phillipines and India show that products from wild IFT species are particularly important to the poorest groups within the community. Dependence on NTFP is in inverse proportion to the size of land holdings and people with little agricultural land are more likely to depend for a goodly part of their income on what they can harvest in wooded areas.

Groups within the community with more land and more income are not strangers to NTFP either. They continue to use them even when living in town though they are much more likely to purchase the items than go out and collect them. The most desired items are seasonal fruits and nuts, teas, spices, leaf wrappings, smokewood, chewsticks, luffa, and materials for handicrafts. Snails, caterpillars and other edible insects should also be considered desired items.

For people who already derive a certain amount of their income and a certain amount of their own food and needs from the forest it is a logical, evolutionary transition to plant purposefully, include or cultivate a useful IFT species near the family home. (See Figure 11 on page 224.)

There the household may benefit from all aspects of the species including its usefulness as a windbreak, shade tree or a living fence. There be may secondary products from the IFT species as well as what was usually harvested in the forest such as leaves or bark for fodder or tea, building material such as fiber or poles. These characteristics or attributes (usually overlooked when a plant is commercially planted) are often underutilized because of the sheer hard work in getting them out of the forest. These underutilized products when found right on the family's doorstep, can make an appreciable difference in the economics of the rural farmstead or household.

Therefore the germplasm promoted for family feeding should include multipurpose species that first supplement and improve the family diet and can be sold or traded—but also can be used in many other ways around the farm or household.

Where IFT species are cultivated or used in the wild there are dozens of candidates for any of these programs or developmental pathways among the IFT species—most notably among the "included species." These "included trees" have been deliberately left on the land when land is cleared for agriculture.

That means the trees have already been evaluated by the farmer and have been left unmolested because the farm household benefits more from this relict representative of the wilderness than a cultivated orchard tree that might be put in its place

From merely "including" a tree to planting it deliberately is a very small step and one of the quicker pathways to domestication.

Raising and harvesting these IFT species allows rural householders particularly woman and children to improve their situation, supplement the family income, provide nutrition for themselves and work toward food security.

Experience with pilot programs has shown that a few good trees, cared for by a poor rural family can produce hundreds of dollars worth of food and materials that would otherwise be unavailable.

Pilot programs have mostly dealt with tropical fruit trees, usually domesticated plants such as oranges, apples, mangoes or dates, all orchard trees with easy to market produce.

These pilot programs have been sponsored by rural development leagues, NGOs and research institutes.

Other organizations and NGOs deal with the promotion of sustainable livelihoods for local people.

These programs concentrate on using fruits, nuts and materials from the local commons in a sustainable manner and emphasize the protection of wild common areas and their careful regeneration.

A program in the Atlas mountains for instance has organized Berber women to protect and replant wild stands of Argania spinosa even as they gather the nuts which they process into oil.

A similar program has been started to encourage stewardship of wild chestnut trees in the mountains of Spain.

An interesting example of an organization promoting this type of land use is MAB (UNESCO's Man And Biosphere project) though this organization and others like it are not as involved in the idea of cultivating IFT species as new crops—but of using properly the wild stands that already exist.

An example of "included" germplasm is the marula tree (Sclerocarya caffra), a key species of arid and semi arid African woodlands. It is also considered one of the most important IFT candidates for family feeding. The tree yields many kilos of fruit under difficult conditions which can be made into a variety of simple VAP. The marula also produces storable nuts which can be eaten or pressed for oil, medicinal bark and excellent wood for carving curios, bowls and spoons.

The main obstacle to the promotion of IFT through family feeding programs is the lack of information about habit, life cycle and potential of the species.

Some IFT species are difficult to acquire. Few have undergone selection and screening and fewer still can be purchased from a plant nursery.

As a result the bush mango is overlooked and the domesticated mango planted instead.

That is why it is important to involve and inform extension services that work with the rural poor. When these institutions are made aware of the potential of local IFT they can be helpful in the distribution of germplasm, provide information about the species, offer suggestions as to cultivation and instructions for production of VAP and marketing of IFT products.

When a household or family feeding program begins these services should be enlisted immediately as well as many knowledgeable local people as can be accommodated by the budget.

Local people can accurately project the food needs of their own households and other households like theirs. They can predict "hungry" seasons and locate flaws in the program designed by outside experts.

Local people can also be the "worker bees" of such efforts distributing information and knowing how and where resources can be deployed effectively.

Fruits of the Future

A program inaugurated in March 2002 called "Fruits of the Future" is a three year project which attempts to contact and inform small holder and farmers of the potential of IFT species semi—domesticated germplasm and fruits of local importance.

This project will also attempt to broaden the knowledge about selected species and bridge gaps in research.

From the Non-wood Forest Products FAO bulletin March 2002

Another aspect of "family feeding" and "sustainable livelihoods" is finding enough food for the family's animals.

This is important for several reasons. The family animals provide what is sometimes the only high protein food available. Poultry hatches out and matures quickly enough to provide rural families with eggs and occasional meat meals. Herd animals are a measure of wealth in many rural economies and kept for their milk—or in some areas for their blood, a resource that is collected without much harm to the animals. Herd animals are also valued for their dung, a resource that may be used as fertilizer, building material and fuel for the household cooking fire.

Even "pets" such as dogs and cats may be very important in the ecology of a farm, the canines as herd dogs, guard dogs and companions and the cats because of their ceaseless hunting of rodents, insects and snakes.

The rural cat or dog usually survives on scraps from the farm kitchen—but the flock or the herd needs a considerably larger amount of food to produce milk or eggs and even more food to be fattened for market.

Successful programs take the needs of the family animals into account and promote IFT crops that can underpin animal feeding as well.

An example of a such a program which utilizes some IFT species can be found in Eritrea where the leaf proteins of desert trees are combined with harvested material from halophytes (salt tolerant plants) and seaweed to produce an animal feed designed to keep animals in condition over the dry season.

The halophytes and seaweed are processed in a manner that de—mineralizes them, then they are combined with leaf protein for added nutrition and bulk.

This program has become so successful that the researchers involved cannot keep up with demand for the new feed.

Another interesting program in Kenya has investigated and promoted the use of the Croton megalocarpus tree to feed and condition poultry.

This species is indigenous to the montane (hilly) forests of East Africa. Its seeds contain over 30% protein and 50% oil and can be ground into a nourishing meal which fed to poultry can substitute for a full half of the high protein, high energy foodstuffs used to produce commercial poultry feed.

Poultry fed on croton meal and local agricultural wastes alone do very well, laying many more eggs and growing faster than free—range chickens fed only on maize.

Utilization of this tree could make the possibility of raising poultry and eggs (and eating them) a reality for poor families.

Certainly IFT should be considered prime candidates for the production of food for livestock, especially the copious bearing trees that produce so much of their primary product so quickly and in such numbers that much of the product is wasted.

A good example of this is the Horse Chestnut tree (Aesculus hippocastanum), a native of northern and central Asia that because of its beauty and hardiness has spread across the temperate and Mediterranean zones. The tree bears truly generous amounts of shiny brown nuts resembling sweet chestnuts but while nutritious, are very bitter. Soaking the nuts in lime water, drying them and grinding them to meal produces a high protein food supplement for farm animals including chickens, turkeys, cattle, horses, goats and sheep. Pigs usually will not eat horse chestnut meal though it is a concentrated very nutritious substance. Experiments during WW1 proved that for every ton of horse chestnuts used for fodder that half a ton of grain could be saved for human consumption. (See Figure 10 on page 224.)

Hardy IFT selections suitable as stock feed trees would be useful on a global, not merely a local scale

To quote J. Russel Smith's book *Tree Crops* published in 1950

*"This book is primarily an attack upon the gully
(erosion). To succeed in this we must have millions
of acres of tree crops replacing destructive plow
crops. Now the nuts that people eat are fine and worthy of much improvement but a few hundred thousand acres of them would glut the market. Not so
with stock food. Once we get a cow feed tree crop
established we have a guaranteed outlet and twenty
or thirty million acres will not glut the market. We
would simply convert thirty or forty million acres out
of our hundred million acres of corn to a more profitable and soil saving crop."*

There is not as of yet a cow feed tree but with a poultry feed tree already undergoing domestication a tree
crop for feeding the meat and milk animals of the
world, a specific tree for this purpose, might not be
far behind.

And it is likely that such a tree will be first identified
because of dire necessity, in a place where corn and
wheat are too precious to be fed to animals and
where the survival of one or two cows through the
dry season is the burning question—not in a place
where the concern is the fattening of a multitude of
gigantic herds.

The Possibility of Stock Feed Trees

Actually feeding stock on the fruits and nuts of
wooded areas is a venerable practice in traditional
agriculture.

To this end the swineherd took his pigs to the oak
groves to fatten on "oaken mast"(a combination of
nuts and fallen leaves) and the goatherd and shep-
herd grazed their animals under the carob trees so
the animals would benefit from the seasonable
bounty of high protein pods.

Other trees which produce leaves, pods and seeds of value to live stock:

The Tamarugo (Prosopis tamarugo) is one of the hardiest and most salt tolerant trees in the prosopis family from the Atacama desert. This tree produces juicy forage and nourishing pods under extremely harsh conditions. It is also an effective windbreak and dune stabilizer suitable for arid and saline areas.

A closely related species, Keawe, the swift growing algaroba (Prosopis chiliensis) that was introduced to Hawaii as an apiary plant in 1860 but showed so much promise as a forage crops that it was seriously researched by the U. S. Dept of Agriculture. One of the facts discovered about this tree was that it was possible to keep stock in groves of Keawe trees for two months each year without giving any other kind of food.

The spiny mesquite (Prosopis juliflora) whose seeds were ground into flour by Native Americans provide an excellent forage for sheep goats and cattle as both the sticky pods, leaves and twigs are full of sugar and protein. (See Figure 9 on page 223.)

The Honey Locust tree, the champion sugar producer of the wild,(Gledetsia triacanthos) is one of the most promising of the potential stock feed trees. A hardy native of North America that can adapt itself to challenging conditions, many honey locust pods contain a staggering 30—35 percentage of sugar. This equals the best sugar beets and puts the troublesome and destructive sugar cane to shame.

The honey locust tree grows quickly, is propagated easily by cuttings or suckers so superior trees can be propagated with a minimum of effort. The tree has excellent timber, it is a legume, and a fine shade or windbreak tree with an open habit.

Among copious bearers of fruits and nuts the American persimmon is of special value for fattening and conditioning animals. All animals kept for meat milk or eggs eat these fruits with enthusiasm and dry fleshed persimmons can be added to silage or stored for months.

Another good stock feed tree is the common mulberry, a tree that underpins the dike/pond integrations of southern China providing food for silkworms, ducks, fish and pigs.

The sweet chestnut tree (Castanea sativa) should not be ignored. It is as close to a "corn tree" as is possible at this point. Its foliage and nuts provided food for pigs, goats, sheep and cattle as well as wood and food for the people who tended the animals. Chestnut fed pork and chevron (goatmeat) are gourmet items in some places in Europe because the meat of chestnut fed animals is leaner and superior in flavor.

Perhaps one of these trees or perhaps an interplanted combination of them will grace the pastures of the future and the precious corn and grain used to fatten meat animals will go instead to human beings who cannot be sure of their daily bread.

Chapter Nine
The Challenge of Multipurpose Species

What is a "Utility Tree"?

A utility tree/multipurpose species is a tree that produces multiple products and serves multiple purposes in the continuum of human use.

A utility tree may supply food for man and forage for animals, shade and shelter, poles and firewood, materials for crafts and building as well as plant material for medicine or dye.

Utility trees are usually rugged plants that produce many offspring and are easy to propagate. They are often useful as windbreaks, living fences or boundary plants. Many utility trees tolerate extreme conditions. Often utility trees are true pioneer plants springing up with weed like vigor after floods or fires and in disturbed earth.

In What Formats and Situations are Utility Trees Most Useful?

Wild Trees

In a wild state the utility tree is a blessing. The primary product may be gathered, the shade and wood enjoyed and other plant parts collected with the only "expense" the labor of the wildcrafter. Such trees bring a cornucopia of benefits to the ecosystem as well shading and cooling the earth, absorbing seasonal water, providing food for wildlife and refuge for pollinators, birds, and other creatures.

Unfortunately wild trees are vulnerable to unwise and unscrupulous use and exploitation. Wild trees are sometimes felled by extractivists too lazy to gather the fruits and products properly. Utility trees with especially hard or valued wood may be timbered off with no thought or understanding of their true value.

Responsible wildcrafters and conservationists react with justifiable horror when the mopane tree is felled to better collect the worms or the bush mango is cut down for firewood.

These local depredations are symptomatic of the erosion of the IFT resource base as a whole and are cause for great concern.

Dooryard Trees and Farmyard Trees

The utility tree is usually spared when the land is cleared because the farmer or gardener wishes to benefit from the range of plant products and plant attributes.

So the indaba tree may stand in the yard or the crab—apple may be left at the bottom of the orchard. The plant products enter the continuum of use in the household and any VAP produced in the home enter the market at its most basic level.

The potential of many IFT species is revealed at this early stage of domestication. The species is now on agricultural land in close proximity to domestic plants and animals. The resourcefulness of the farmer and the reservoir of local knowledge allow for the utilization of the tree for maximum possible benefits. A great deal of informal experimentation occurs in the household as the plant products are measured against local needs and tastes.

Included IFT species, sometimes called "dooryard trees" are no longer truly wild. Much is known about their uses, products, propagation and life cycle. A good deal of the necessary work of domestication has been done. Included IFT and the people who use, tend and appreciate included plants are immensely important in IFT research and should be valued by scientists and researchers accordingly.

Owned Trees

The small domestic format is another stage in the domestication pathway. Sometimes called the "pocket orchard" it refers to orchards and groves that are part of the local commons. The grove is sometimes of natural origin and preserved by local consensus with relatively consistent and orderly harvesting by specific families and individuals. In some cases the orchard or grove has been planted deliberately, in which case the trees may be "owned" though they may not be anywhere near the property of the person who makes the claim. Indeed "owned" trees can sometimes be found in what are essentially wilderness areas. A good example of "owned " trees in jungles and forests are Asia's durian trees. These large and beautiful trees produce the big, strong smelling and extremely valuable durian fruit, a fruit that has to be cracked out of a formidable spiked outer shell. Durian trees often bear a tag or mark to indicate their status and should be considered semi domesticated rather than wild germplasm. Boabab trees in Africa are often owned trees. (See Figure 12 on page 225.)

Utility trees are esteemed in this format. Their attributes and satellite products are of such value to the rural communities that the distances the products must be carried and the relative inaccessibility of the trees do not preclude harvest and use.

Gum and Butter Parks

Gum and butter parks are the regenerative stage of long cycle agricultural rotations in arid areas or areas with poor soil. After four or five years of continuous cropping the African farmer moves to another plot of land leaving the first plot fallow or to be used as pasture. Acacia trees or other IFT species are allowed to invade and after they have grown up the trees are tapped for gum or their seeds are gathered to make oil ("butter"). During this period of the rotation the soil is protected by tree cover. Falling leaves build up a layer of litter that allows nutrients and humus to accumulate in the topsoil. Fertility is often enhanced by nitrogen fixing bacteria in the tree roots. "Gum and butter" species are often utility trees, such as the acacia, the mimusops or the shea butter tree.

The primary product is used or sold and other products of the tree such as nectar, bark and flowers enter the market as spices or materia medica.

In this format the vigorous pioneering qualities of the utility trees are vital in the establishment of tree cover to mitigate temperature and protect the topsoil. The abundant foliage of the tree enriches the soil. The powerful root system works against the forces of erosion and encourages the infiltration of water into the soil

Integrations

Arboreal integrations that contain many species in deliberate imitation of natural forest are much enriched by the inclusion of utility trees. In this format the physical properties of the tree can be appreciated. Utility trees shade weaker and slower growing species and protect them from the weather. The powerful root systems of the utility tree have a regenerative effect on compacted and depleted ground. Foliage, twigs and fruit enrich the soil, attract wildlife and provide benefits for domesticated animals.

Agroforesry and Reforested Areas

The vigor of the utility tree and their weed like characteristics are beneficial for reforestation and agroforestry projects—especially when the plantings have been made to combat wind and water erosion. Large quick growing trees with spreading root systems and dense crowns stabilize denuded soil quickly. Since the pioneering qualities of most utility trees indicate quick growth and a tendency to dominate replanted areas it may be necessary to thin out utility trees at some point and introduce other species in the clearings.

Plantings made to stabilize ground water problems also benefit from the presence of multipurpose species especially those tolerant of saline or heavily mineralized water.

Where Utility Trees Are More Problematic

Parks and Urban Areas

Utility trees are sometime problematic as decorative plants—the exception being the males of some species. The male trees have the strength, hardiness and beauty of the female but not the potentially troublesome primary product. An example of this type of tree is the male gingko tree.

The female gingko tree produces copious amounts of strong smelling fruit that are smashed onto paths and lawns. Many municipalities have forbidden the planting of female gingko trees for this reason. On the other hand, the male tree, that produces harmless quantities of flowers, is one of the species of choice in urban plantings. Another example is the male marula tree, a shade tree of unusual beauty, without the problem of the hundreds of kilos of marula fruit which abcisse from the female plant and lie around in fermenting heaps.

Plantations

Utility trees are generally unappreciated in large plantation formats. Plantation agriculture evolves around the swift mass production of one primary product. Usually other possible products are discarded, ignored or considered nuisances to be gathered up and destroyed.

Host Trees, Foodstocks

The mopane tree hosts the valuable and nutritious mopane worm, the mulberry tree feeds the silkworm, the carob tree produces carob mast to feed the goats.

Pigs can feed on the leaves and nuts of the oak trees that are sometimes the host trees for the rare and expensive edible fungi, the truffle.

Organisms associated with IFT species can be of great value to the farm or the ecosystem in their own right. Many host trees and fodder or mast producing trees are multi-purpose species.

It is important to plant utility trees in formats in which they can be appreciated holistically and their products utilized fully and wisely.

Sample Evaluation of common IFT species as utility trees

Common name: Marula

Latin name and family Sclerocarya cafra from the family Anacardiacae

Description: A large spreading tree with pale bark and blue green leaves, deciduous and dioecious. Female flowers are small and inconspicuous while male flowers are catkin—like. The tree's small mango—like fruits abcisse and fall before ripening.

Products: marula trees produce fruits that may be eaten fresh, made into beer, jam, liquor, sweets, and kamaradin or fed to animals. The kernels within the marula fruit's hard seeds may be roasted and eaten or pressed into useful oil. Marula wood is pale with a red grain and suitable for carving. Marula trees may be coppiced or thinned for poles, surplus male trees may be used as decorative plants or culled for lumber. Marula bark is a reported medicinal and an anti—malarial.

Attributes: Marula trees are fast growing, hardy, tolerant of drought and salinity, some trees are tolerant of low temperatures (Botswannan marulas especially) and all are tolerant of very high temperatures. Copious amount of seeds are produced by the tree and root suckers may be used for propagation. Seeds should be drilled, cracked or aged before planting or many will not sprout. The tree has a spreading habit and mulches itself with piles of fallen leaves but can be trained to grow with a single central trunk.

Potential: The marula has great potential in all previously named formats from dooryard trees to commercial orchards, even as a decorative plant if only male trees are used. As a crop the marula could develop in three directions, as a table fruit crop, an oil—producing crop or as raw material for alcoholic beverages.

Common name: Argania

Latin name and family: Argania spinosa from the family Sapotacae

Description: A thorny small leafed hardwood, slow growing, long lived and nicknamed ironwood. The argania's flowers are perfect and very small clustering on young branches in the internodal areas. The whole fruit looks like a plump green olive. The nut inside resembles an acorn and the oil—bearing kernel is like a small flat almond. Argania nuts fall when the outer fleshy layer turns yellow.

Products: Argania fruits may be harvested and dried. The outer layer can be cracked off to feed animals, the nut shells can be used to make fiberboard and the kernal pressed into superior edible oil or processed into the traditional nut butter "**amalou**," a traditional food made from the argania oil and ground almonds.

Argania wood is extremely hard, resistant to weather and insects. The trees may be coppiced to produce durable poles. Argania leaves and twigs are preferred forage for camels and goats.

Attributes: Argania trees are very drought tolerant and can survive for years with little water, re—sprouting miraculously when the rains fall again. Argania roots delve deeply in search of water penetrating compacted and rocky soils, stopping erosion in dunes and sandy areas. These qualities make argania very valuable in desert plantings. The argania tree is a preferred nesting site for birds and a source of food for animals that consume the outer layer of fruit pulp and leave or expel the indigestible nut. Argania trees are easy to propagate by seeds. While vegetative propagation is more difficult it is possible to propagate superior individual trees by taking cutting of older tissues and using growth hormones to induce rooting.

Potential: Argania has great potential as a multipurpose crop plant in arid and semi arid areas. It is suitable for permacultural plantings, gum and butter parks and terraces in marginal or eroded areas.

Argania has the potential to be the "olive" of the arid sub tropics.

Common name: Tamarind.

Latin name and family name: Tamarindus indica from the family Leguminosae.

Description: A tall tree,one of the great trees of the tropics, with gray—brown bark, lush pinnate leaves., red racemes with yellow veined petals and large cinnamon brown pods containing unusually shaped seeds in a thin membrane. The pods are rich in sugars and acids.

Products: The tamarind pods are a source of drinks, flavoring, vitamin rich additions to staple foods, sauces such as Worchestershire and Picakpeppa, chutney, pickles and medicinal products. The seeds are a source of gum used in textiles and oil suitable for the production of varnish. The tamarind leaves and branches are a good source of food for animals (The animals can also be fed with waste pulp from tamarind pod processing). The wood is strong and easy to work. Poles may be cut from mature trees. The tree is a nitrogen fixing legume ideal for enriching poor soils, the flowers are a rich source of nectar for birds, bees and other pollinators and can be used to feed silkworms. In addition to its other qualities, the tamarind is one of the finest shade trees in the world, densely crowned and stately. The tamarind is tolerant of heat, dryness and limited salinity though the best growth occurs in tropical and subtropical areas.

Potential: The tamarind, an exception to the notion that multipurpose trees do not belong in parks and urban settings, is suitable for urban areas, as well as orchards, agroforestry projects and private gardens. This is because its pods are not soft, messy or attractive to insects. The tree can be planted in arid zones and areas with brackish water. The tamarind is an excellent tree as an ornamental, a shade tree or a windbreak. The tamarind is especially suitable in food forests, cloud gardens and other permacultural integrations as it supports the existence of so many benign organisms.

How to Determine If An IFT Species Is A Utility Tree/Multipurpose Species

The following checklist should help a farmer or researcher focus on the attributes of specific IFT species.

If four or more questions are answered in the affirmative then care should be taken to develop and domesticate the species holistically and to use all products and attributes.

1. **Primary Products**: Does the IFT species produce a primary product such as edible fruits, pods or nuts?
2. **Secondary Products**: Does the IFT species produce secondary products such as fiber, bark, poles thatch, burls or other craft or building materials?
3. **Tertairy products**: Does the IFT species produce tertiary products such as teas or spices?
4. **Forage, fodder or mast**: Can the IFT species be used for animal feeding?
5. **Host plant**: Is the IFT species a host plant for beneficial organisms such as silkworms, mopanae worms, edible fungi ?
6. **Apiary plant**: Is the IFT species a source of pollen or nectar?
7. **Medicinal plant**: Is the IFT species a source for materia medica?
8. **Integrations**: Is the IFT species useful as a nurse tree, pioneer plant, natural trellis?
9. **Rare substances**: Does the species produce gums, resins, smokewood, incense, oil or any other rare substance?

10.**Margins**: Does the species perform well as a wind-break, living fence, hedge, barrier, buffer or boundary plant for alley cropping?
11.**Cultural**: Does this species have a ritual, cultural or social dimension?

Two examples of evaluation of a species by these criteria follow: the date and the willow

---

The Date Tree. (Phoenix dactylifera)

Primary product: The date is a very nourishing fruit with high trade value which can be sold fresh or dried or made into VAP including, alcohol, sweets, baked goods, flavoring, filling and syrup.

Secondary product: The date tree produces fiber for crafts and fronds for fences, roofs, thatch and bas-ket—weaving.

Forage: Culled or spoiled dates can be fed to live-stock.

Medicinal: The fruit of the date tree has medicinal properties

Integretions: The date tree can provide protection and shade for more fragile crops and stabilize high, saline water tables in an integrated or permacultural format.

Margins: Rows of date trees make excellent wind-breaks tolerant of sandstorms, and flash flooding.

Cultural: The date tree is important religiously and culturally to Middle Eastern people including Beduin, Jews, Kurds, Druse and Arabs.

The Willow (Salix alba)

Secondary product: The willow produces withies or supple branches for crafts.

Forage: Animals will browse on willow twigs and leaves

Medicinal: Willow bark is the source of natural aspirin.

Integrations: Willows are planted to absorb and control excess water.

Margins: Willows protect riparian areas, preserve the integrity of river banks and provide buffer zones as well as being planted as living fences and garden barriers.

Cultural: The willow is sacred to a variety of people world wide and used in many rites and ceremonies

In conclusion it might be said that numerous IFT species may fit the given definition a multipurpose species or "utility tree"

But domesticated formats do not usually encourage the development or use of the species beyond the harvesting of the most obvious primary product.

If multipurpose IFT species are to be domesticated in a way which utilizes their products, characteristics and attributes fully and sensibly it is the format of cultivation that must be rethought and remade.

Chapter Ten
The IFT species in Agroforestry and Related Activities

The simplest definition of agroforestry is the production of trees, tree crops and non tree crops on the same piece of land. Agroforestry projects can be completely integrated or crops can be grown separately. Some projects are extremely integrated and attempt to mimic forest ecosystems. Other projects resemble commercial tree plantations and truck farms with little biodiversity.

Still most agroforestry projects adhere somewhat to the ethic and intent of *"stewardship"* and because of this should be appreciated and encouraged for their virtues rather than condemned for their faults.

Agroforestry systems attempt to make maximum use of the land by planting perennial multipurpose crops that protect, improve or maintain the soil and the watershed and to produce a range of benefits including food for humans and animals, raw materials for medicine, building materials, shade, climatic mitigation and renewed fertility.

The physical attributes of selected tree species are used to hold the soil, fix nitrogen in the soil, bring minerals up from deep in the soil and deposit leaves and plant material as natural mulch and soil cover.

Crop interactions and competition between species are considered as well as species needs for air, light water and soil nutrition.

Agroforestry projects are one class of projects among many modern attempts to manage large arboreal plantings, enriched plantings or protected natural forests for the benefit of the local ecosystem, local wildlife and local human population.

Balancing the needs of all the creatures and organisms concerned is no easy task and it is no wonder that the concept of agroforestry remains a little nebulous and that so many versions of agroforestry plantings and reforestation activities have come into being around the world.

To simplify matters it is possible to divide these strategies roughly into six categories by their ultimate goals rather than their interim practices.

Reclamation

Land reclamation attempts to achieve stability and productivity on degraded land but does not attempt to return local biodiversity.

Reclamation is often done with non—native species and puts the reclaimed ecosystem to a new or altered use.

Rehabilitation

Land rehabilitation attempts to make the land useful, stable and productive again using original species(plus introduced species when necessary) and to reestablish some ecological functions.

Reforestation

Attempts to restore forest cover to areas where the natural forest cover has been lost due to human induced harvesting or natural perturbations.

Afforestation

Afforestation attempts to establish a ground cover of trees, shrubs and grasses on barren land or land where no forest has existed in recent years.

Restoration

Restoration forestry attempts to reestablish the presumed structure and components of the original ecosystem and recreate the systems self—sustaining dynamic.

Commerical Agroforestry

Commercial Agroforestry is a land use system in which woody perennials such as palms, shrubs, trees, bamboo or other woody perennials are deliberately included in the same land management unit as agricultural crops, agricultural animals or both.

Very specific variations of agroforestry are done for very specific purposes.

Some examples follow.

Alley cropping: Growing annual crops between rows of trees that provide protection and soil enrichment.

Beautification plantings: Ornamental planting in areas destroyed or depleted by human activity usually in or close to urban settings.

Boundary planting: planting rows or trees or small copses to mark off areas specific to use or to individual landowners.

Dispersed plantings: Trees are scattered across the landscape often to improve drainage or provide shade for animals.

Dike plantings and earthwork plantings: Trees or other perennials are planted on dikes and earthworks to stabilize them and protect them from erosion.

Improved fallows: Areas planted with soil enriching trees as part of crop rotation.

Living fences: Trees that serve as fences to keep animals in or out.

Wind—breaker trees: lines or copses of tree planted to protect crops, roads, or dwellings.

Liman plantings: a system of planting individual trees by shaping a water collecting area and planting a seedling when the collected water gathers (used in arid areas).

Nectar plantings: Groves of trees planted to provide nectar and pollen for bees.

Terrace planting: Perennial plants introduced to leveled areas along the contours of hills, usually for watershed protection and erosion control.

Vegetative strips: Long narrow areas of trees and perennial plants used to control erosion, mitigate noise, absorb pollution, improve air quality, usually near roads or in areas prone to flooding.

Woodlots: Areas planted to trees used for fuel or timber.

The many benefits of agroforestry systems can be summarized:

- Improved production of food and useful products
- Employment opportunities
- Soil protection and improvement, erosion control
- Mitigation and beautification of urban environments and areas near roads
- Increased efficiency in land use
- Shade, windbreaks and climatic mitigation
- Protection of non—tree agriculture
- Increased wildlife habitat
- Increase of fuel and timber availability
- Increased availability of nectar and shelter for beneficial insects.

For our purposes it is possible to assign these disciplines to four situations in which IFT species can be included:

- projects in natural forests (restoration, rehabilitation)
- projects in enrichment plantings(reclamation, afforestation)
- specialized plantings (improved fallows etc.)
- and projects in reforested areas (agroforestry, reforestation).

The individual IFT species may play a different role in each niche or unit of land management.

IFT species In A Natural Forest

This version of forest management is very close to what is currently called "sustainable management" NWFP (non wood forest products) are harvested, access is limited to a licensed or tenured group to avoid over—utilization of the resources. There may be hunting of wildlife or other population adjustment if one kind of animal begins to overbreed the environment but basically the extraction of wild meat, fruit, nuts, craft material and medicinals is controlled. The managed forest is usually patrolled by forest service employees such as rangers or game wardens with detailed census of plants and animals taken every year. Fallen trees are cleared to decrease the chance of wildfire and young native trees are planted, very often IFT species. The area may be fenced or posted. The rationale behind this type of agoforestry is a conserving one, attempting to manage the forest holistically with agricultural crops and animals confined to the periphery and the core of the forest protected.

IFT In Enrichment Plantings

Enrichment plantings are usually established to help regenerate a damaged or eroded ecosystem often as one facet of what is called rehabilitation or "restoration ecology." This type of planting is very useful in areas that have been logged and are now getting secondary growth, areas that have been damaged by fire, acid rain or other weather events and marginal lands that need to be reclaimed from aridity or salinity because of unwise agricultural practices.

Vigorous and fast growing pioneer plants that can supply food for wild life are often among the first plants chosen for enrichment plantings.

A good example of this kind of IFT is the black buckthorn (Rammus alpinus) which colonizes dry and stony slopes at 800 to 1000 meters. Its fruits are the preferred food by many animals including bears. The leaves and flowers of the buckthorn are browsed by deer, goats and chamois. The bark of the black buckthorn has medicinal properties and the wood makes good charcoal. The berries can be eaten or cooked into preserves and are a source of cosmetic oil.

Most importantly the black buckthorn prepares the slopes for the reintroduction of conifers and other trees by increasing soil infiltration of rainwater, enriching the soil with humus, providing shade and ground cover that allows soil organisms to regenerate and by bringing wildlife back into the area.

The black buckthorn is a temperate zone plant but sea buckthorn (Hipophae rhamnoides) has been used to colonize dry, saline, degraded and desolate areas in China. There this plant has been planted out over huge areas to stop the spread of sand dunes into cultivated lands. The fruits are eaten by wildlife and can be made into half a dozen simply produced types of VAP. The tangled thickets of sea buckthorn provide cover for birds and animals and protection for slower growing plants and saplings. After sea buckthorn has colonized an area it is much easier to reintroduce trees and other types of plants.

Enrichment plantings usually deal with a succession of different reintroduced plants and colonizations, each step bringing an area closer to what is believed to be the natural forest cover of the area before depredations by the human population.

IFT in specialized agroforestry

The underutilized IFT species contain such a range of potentially useful trees with such a great wealth of tolerances, resistances and characteristics that IFT role in specialized agroforestry projects is growing from year to year especially in the most challenging environments. The projects in African and Asia dealing with improved fallows are a good example.

IFT in Reforested Areas and Planned Agroforestry Integrations.

Reforestation: Most agroforestry planting have been designed for specific purposes relating to land reclamation, reforestation or stabilization of ground water. There are very few agroforestry projects that have been planted, managed and maintained solely to produce food.

But food production and the production of useful materials are both very important goals of the agroforestry of the developing world—plants which produce one or more useful or edible materials make up one half to two thirds of the species chosen for reforestation in Africa and Asia. These species may be chosen for their physical properties or their usefulness as fuel, lumber or forage as well but a high percentage of reforested acres have been replanted with trees that supply edible primary products that can be utilized by man or returning wildlife.

Food Forests: In a planned integration the percentage of IFT species that produce edible primary products is much higher. Every tree in a planned agroforestry integration has been chosen because it fulfills several roles in a deliberately created miniature ecosystem. The species are chosen because of their value as food producers, shade plant, trellis plants, soil restorers, source of useful materials, value to animal feeding and value to beneficial organisms within the planting.

For example in a dry area the carob tree may be planted to produce pods for human use or mast for animal feeding, enrich the soil with fallen leaves, break up dry stony or compacted ground with its strong root net, draw bees and other pollinators into the plantings with its masses of male and female flowers and lower ground temperatures because of the shade cast by its dense broad leafed crown.

In an area with more rainfall and humidity the tamarind tree might be chosen to fulfill similar functions.

The Potential of IFT in Agroforestry

With some work and investigation IFT species can fit nicely in all of these formats.

Replanting IFT species in a managed natural forest or protecting existing IFT stands confers a range of benefits on the forest ecosystem, supporting birds, insects, wildlife and human extractivism.

In enrichment plantings the IFT species chosen for pioneering and regenerative roles can have a profound influence on the rate and state of the chosen areas recovery.

In reforested areas and planned integrations the IFT species physical properties can truly be appreciated as well as their food producing capabilities.

Since agroforestry, reforestation and restoration projects must be carefully designed temporally as well as spatially and ecologically, species with short juvenile periods and swift growth are often chosen for initial plantings.

Other IFT species, including slow growing species can be included in successive stages of planting when the harshness of the damaged environment has already been mitigated by the presence of the stronger pioneering species.

Reclamation and afforestation

IFT species are not always seen as important resources in the context of reclamation.

In some variations of land reclamation IFT species are not included:

Single purpose plantings: This is a planting strategy of desperation, designed to stop erosion, stabilize slopes and introduce greenery at all costs. Strong-rooting, hardy plants are introduced to an area sometimes as monocultures—usually with little regard for anything but the physical properties of the plant. Diversification of plant life and successive plantings will only be done after the basic problem has been solved and the loss of topsoil halted.

These areas are usually biological deserts having been planted with eucalyptus, casuarinas or fast growing pines. They rarely include IFT species and while the plantings could produce teas, nuts, bark, charcoal and medicinals if harvested in a sustainable manner the areas are almost never harvested.

The trees are simply "there" stopping the soil wash which would otherwise lead to a terminal state of land degradation and that is enough for the advocates of this kind of reclamation.

There are many projects of this type all over the world usually filling the void where a natural forest was destroyed or cut down—and not filling it very well.

IFT species are not always desired in afforesation projects, many which impose new patterns on a landscape and introduce non—native trees and shrubs. In this format IFT species are sometimes seen as "messy" because of the primary products that may attract animals, birds and insects into the planted area.

In contrast, in the management of relict and old growth woodlands IFT species play a vital role:

Managing relict forests and old growth woods

A vital strategy concerns managing and defending old growth woodlands that have not been logged. Some of these areas are the remnants of huge forests, spared for now from development. Other areas are vast and still almost untouched ecosystems.

These areas and their IFT species and wildlife must be protected from the plow, the chain saw and the bulldozer. In order to do this it is first necessary to gain some legal recognition for the value of these woods.

This means involving the local and national governments and convincing them of the value of the forests as watersheds and preserves for unique animals and plants. It may be necessary to convince the governments that the forests will attract eco—tourists or to point out that bio—prospecting has become big business. It will be necessary to emphasize over and over again the **uniqueness and potential value** of the **forest products.**

It is also necessary to impress the local and national government as to the value of the socio—ecological systems that have grown up with these forests and to seek legal protection for the rights of the people who live in the forests to their land, their lifestyle and to the benefits of what is extracted from the ancient groves.

Often rescue and conserving management can only be achieved if rival professions, clans, tribes, families and interest groups put aside their differences and unite to protect their shared commons.

Sometimes rescue and preservation can be achieved only if local people become activists, taking the initiative to save the botanical and biological treasures around their homes.

Luckily they do not have to stand alone against the forces of unwise exploitation, there are many organizations and institutions that can help by supplying funds, offering legal advice, expertise and plans for sustainable management and use.

The Example of the Minombo Woodlands

The attempt to save and manage the Minombo woodlands is an example of cooperation between local people, national governments and international institutions.

This vast area drawn on by an estimated 40 million people for food, fuel wood and building materials is a truly unique ecosystem with over 180 species of IFT and thousands of rare herbs, shrubs, birds and animals.

The initiative is a collaborative one between the governments of Malawi, Mozambique Tanzania, Zimbabwe and Zambia with the help of CIFOR and the European Union.

The goal of the project is to formulate the guidelines and gain the knowledge necessary to mange the woodlands while improving protective measures and promoting the welfare of the people who depend on them.

This is only one of dozens of research projects and initiatives around the world dedicated to the preservation and sustainable management of wild lands and wild plant resources and granting belated recognition to the importance of IFT species.

Chapter Eleven
Rare Substances from IFT Species

What is a "rare substance"?

How can the value and scarcity of these rare substances preserve IFT species and provide livelihoods for local people?

The first question requires a lengthy answer as there are many substances produced by IFT species that are unusual and many others that are very useful and valuable.

Rare Substances produced by IFT species

1. **Oils** that are pressed or distilled from seeds, nuts, flowers, bark, wood or leaves.
   a. Edible oils: argania, olive, shea butter (from the tree Vitellaria paradoxus), bush olive, Indian almond, zycum oil (from the tree Balanites aegypticus)
   b. Medicinal oils: argania, Ti tree oil, (See Figure 21 on page 229)
   c. Cosmetic oil:argania, marula, sea buckthorn
   d. Aromatic oil: sandalwood, eagle wood, mesquite
   e. Special properties jojoba oil, tung oil,. False shea butter (from the seeds of Mimusops elengi)
2. **Medicinals**
   a. "Rain forest" drugs: pau d'arco, boldo, quinine, periwinkle
   b. Herbals: leaves and lesser associated plants such as forest herbs
   c. Teas: special teas that are often made from leaves, bark and flowers
   d. Materia medica: may include roots or any

other plant part
3. **Spice**: Edible spices in the form of fruits, bark, flowers buds and leaves
   a. Pungent spices from fruits such as peppercorns
   b. Flower buds such as cloves or capers
   c. Aromatic seeds or fruit such as nutmeg, mace, allspice
   d. Aromatic bark such as cassia or cinnamon
   e. Pollen as a spice or aromatic such as saffron
   f. Substances that can be used as coloring or flavoring.
4. **Gums** may be collected directly from the plants in the form of sap or may be pressed or extracted from any other plant part. Gums which are harvested directly are usually called exudates.

   A. **Exudates**—these gums are harvested after sap flow is enhanced by incising the bark of the gum tree.
   1. **Gum Arabic** from Acacia Senegal and other acacias used extensively as a stabilizer in the food industry and added to instant soups and mixes. Gum Arabic is also used in the making of ink. art materials, lotions, cosmetics and baked goods.
   2. **Gum karyana** collected from the tree Sterculia urens in dry areas of India and used in toiletry items and pharmaceuticals. Karyana gum is also used to stabilize protein foams and prevent ice crystal growth in frozen foods.
   3. **Gum ghatti** from the tree Anogeissus litifolia in India is used as a stabilizer for oil soluble vitamins, similar to gum Arabic in its properties.
   4. **Gum tragacanth** is collected from Astralagus gummifer bush that grows in semi arid areas of the Middle East and is used as a low

ph emulsion stabilizer, providing body and texture to low calorie products and stabilizing frozen foods which are acidic.

5. **Chios mastic** collected from small twisted trees (Shchinos pistacia) on the Greek isle of Chios. This gum is used in much the same manner as gum Arabic in the making of pigments and circuit boards. Confusingly enough it is sometimes called gum Arabic when sold off island. On the island it is know as Chios mastic and used by the locals as a resinous alternative to chewing gum.

6. **Treetap** also known as "organic" leather specially processed sustainably tapped rubber from wild rubber trees in the Amazon basin.

B. **Extracts:** These gums are extracted from other plant parts of wild species

   1. **Guar gum** is produced from the ground up endosperm of the decorticated seeds of a legume called Cyanopsis tetragonolobus that grows in the semi arid areas of India. Guar gum is used to make gluten free bread, shampoo, paints and pigments.

   2. **Carob gum** a gum that is extracted from the bean of the carob plant (Ceretonia siliqua) The bean is found at intervals along the edible pod, so regular in size that it was once used as a unit in weight for precious stones and metals. Carob gum is used in fabrics, dyes, paints as an adhesive and as a stabilizer in processed foods.

   3. **Psyllium seed gum** from the plantago species of the Mediterranean is used medicinally as a mild laxative and soothing substance irritated membranes.

   4. **Quince seed gum,** this gum is extracted from the from the fruit tree Cydonia

oblonga and is used to make marmalades and preserves as well as hair lotions and gels.

5. **Tamarind gums** from the processed pods of the tamarind are used as stabilizers and thickeners in food, as a binder in tablets and in fabric processing, especially for cotton and jute cloths.

6. **Tara gum** from the milled seeds of Caesalprina shrubs can be used much as carob gum is used.

7. **Fenugreek gum** from the ripe fruits of Trigoneela foenumgraecum is used in curries, imitation maple syrup and pharmaceuticals such as cough syrup.

8. **Aloe gums and saps** are used to make cosmetics, skin lotions, shampoos, salve for burns and skin lesions.

9. **Chia gum** from the edible seeds of the shrub Salvia hispanica has mucilaginous properties at low aqueous concentrations, cosmetic properties and keeps other materials from drying out.

10. **Okra gum** is extracted from the pods of Ablemoschis esculents and can be whipped into a stable foam used in the making of candies and confections.

11. **Yellow mustard** gum is used as a binder and an anti—oxidant in processed food.

5. **Sources of Pectins**: Pectins are used in making jams and jellies and in stabilizing fermented milk products such as fruit yogurt. These sources of pectin could be useful in the small—scale production of forest products from IFT species, they already have considerable value in the current marketplace.

A. **Citrus peel**, the peels of lemons oranges, kumquats, limes, citrons can be processed to yield both pectin and aromatic oils.

B. **Apples** domesticated apples are a fine source of pectin but they are often bested by the crab apple which contains more pectin in the skin and flesh of their smaller and knottier fruits.

C. **Quince** both the seed and the fruit of the quince contain pectin and domesticated varieties of the tree are as pectin rich as wild quinces.

D. **Zisiphus jujube**, the small, dry red fruits of the "Chinese date" are very rich in pectin.

E. **Zisiphus Mauritania** the larger more apple—like fruits of this species are rich in both pectin and sugar.

6. **Starch**: Edible starch and starch for other purposes such as textiles papermaking and adhesives may be obtained from some wild species.

Arrowroots: These wild plants are excellent sources of arrowroot starch.

- Tacca
- Canna
- Curcurma
- Maranta

Though they are not technically trees, some of them are sizable plants, especially in areas with good rainfall and produce roots weighing several kilos. The natural rich biodiversity of these species makes them excellent candidates for immediate domestication.

Starch is extracted from Sago palms such as Metroxylon sagu and other starch producing species such as the Raphia palm, the Fishtail palm, the Sugar palm and the Nipa palm.

Among these palms only the Fishtail palm is commonly cultivated the others are semi domesticated or completely wild. Many other wild species are used in a similar manner to produce starch sugar, drinks and building or craft material.

The Sago Palm

Sago starch is extracted from the Sago palm (Metroxylon sagu) and several other palms and cycads those in the families of Arenga, Cary-old,Eugeissonia.

The sago palm is found naturally in New Guinea in large dense stands in swampy areas. The leaves of the palm are pinnate. The tall heavy trunks accumulate starch. Just before flowering the trunk is cut and prepared for the extraction of starch. Harvesting can be done sustainably because cutting a mature truck encourages basal sprouts to grow and replace it. The harvested trunk is spilt open to reveal soft wood completely permeated by starch granules. The wood and starch are ground and pounded together and immersed in water. The wood floats and can be skimmed away the starch sinks to the bottom of the vessel. After several washings the starch is pure and can be dried in the sun or parched over a fire. The pith of the Sago palm is also used and the material left over after starch extraction can be fed to animals.

The Nipa palm (Nypa fruiticans)

Mentioned in the section 8 as a source of sugary sap, the Nipa palm can also be harvested for sago. The Nipa grows in muddy soils and estuaries where the water is quite brackish and propagates itself by floating seeds and by underground stems which develop into new palm plants. The plants flower stalk is usually tapped for sugary sap but older trunks are sometimes cut for starch and the starch extraction process is very much like that of the sago palm. The Nipa palm fronds are useful in weaving and thatching.

Raphia palms (Raphia sp.)

Raphia palms (Raphia sp.) grow principally in West Africa, there are eight useful species adapted to swampy conditions but able to colonize slightly drier areas as well. The fronds of the Raphia palms are very long and contain strong fibers that can be used like twine and rope. The palms are also a source of both sugary sap and sago.

The Fishtail Palm (Caryota urens)

The Fishtail Palm (Caryota urens) is an adaptable plant that was domesticated in the 12th century and is now cultivated in India, Sri Lanka and suitable areas in Southeast Asia. It is the principle source for commercial palm sugar, the sweet sap being reduced into crumbling light brown rounds of sugar, something like maple sugar in texture. Its doubly pinnate fronds are used in construction. Though the trunks contain good quality starch it is rarely used for sago as it is more valuable as a sugar producing plant.

The Sugar palm.

In India and Southeast Asia the Arenga pinnata is especially planted for sugar production. It is a solitary palm, propagated by seed or offshoot and considered semi—domesticated germplasm rather than a true crop plant. The palm both fruits and flowers copiously. The many inflorescenses both male and female are tapped for sap and the fruit is harvested for its edible kernel as the fruit itself is inedible.

7. **Cellulose and lignocellulose** are valuable in the manufacture of binders, emulsifiers, pharmaceuticals and cosmetics. These substances are only identified by analysis of the wood. Extraction can be a long and complicated process so these substances are most likely to be discovered and utilized if the species is already under some kind of format of use or investigation.

8. **Sap:** Sap is distinguished from gum by the type and percentage of solids—all trees have sap but few produce gum. Many useful substances can be made or extracted from tree sap or sap like substances found in twigs, fruit, pods and seeds.
   a. edible syrups such as those made of pressed carob pods or the sap of maple trees
   b. soft drinks based on sap or sap—like substances such as birch beer, cashew apple nectar or tamarind juice
   c. incense from sap such as that of the myrrh tree (see Figure 20 on page 228) or the frankincense tree (ee Figure 22 on page 229)
   d. Sap which can be made into rubber from rubber trees (Havea sp) or shrubs such as the guayle (Partentium argentatum)
   e. Sap that is made into toddy, jaggery or other beverages such as the sap of the Sugar palm or the Nipa palm.

9. **Miscellaneous rare properties**—there is some overlap in this category as some species have multiple products or purposes
   a. smokewood that burns aromatically (for cooking or incense)
   b. coloring or dyes such as red sandalwood or yehib (Cordeuxia edulis) leaves
   c. craft material such as withies, material for baskets, carving or raffia work
   d. pith such as that from the kaypok or balsa tree (See Figure 19 on page 228)

e. fibers such as those of the mazri palm and from the ceiba tree's flowers
f. host trees for useful or edible insects, such as silkworms, mopane worms or snails.
g. Host tree for truffles, mushrooms or bracket fungi
h. Trees and plants that produce leaves used as salad, leaf protein or leaf wrappings.

How can IFT species that produce such substances be used for the benefit of the local human population?

How can the IFT species be protected from over-utilization or extinction if demand increases for these substances?

To name a few recently discovered substances in very rare trees: The bintagor tree is a huge rubber producing tree. The milky sticky poisonous latex contains a substance that combats HIV/ AIDS and tuberculosis.

The substance the latex yields is processed into a drug called Calanolide A, a very promising "rainforest drug", one of the many medicinal species of plants recently discovered and investigated in the jungles of the southern hemisphere.

While plant prospecting in this manner is necessary to find the medicines of tomorrow, problems can arise when a discovery is made.

The local people, who have often tipped the researcher or plant hunter off to the existence of a botanical treasure, are often left out of the picture regarding possible profit and future development.

Furthermore if the drug produced from the sap of the bintagor tree successfully cures or combats HIV or resurgent tuberculosis the entire species could be at risk of over—utilization or extinction.

Researchers returning to collect more material from the tested tree found it had been felled for fuel or timber. A desperate search for more trees of the same kind ensued and finally trees were found in the Singapore Botannical Garden, collected by the British when the bintagor was more common in the wild.

These are some of the pitfalls of IFT development and must be avoided.

The interests of the local people and the well being of that plants must be safeguarded from the very first steps in domestication to the marketing of the final product.

This should include royalty arrangements or profit sharing for the local people so they have some stake in the development and preservation of the resource.

The plants themselves must be protected by conserving interesting plant populations in situ as well as keeping specific plant types in working collections and seed banks.

In this way the rights of local people are protected and the plants are safe from the danger of extinction, two situations that benefit the biosphere as a whole.

We do not know which strands in the webs of life are directly relevant to our own wellbeing. But unraveling the threads before we know their place and importance can only lead to disaster.

Causing harm on a local level and endangering the existence of an IFT species during the course of its development cannot be considered **"the price of progress."**

Chapter Twelve
Medicinal IFT

Many IFT species have medicinal properties, sometimes present in the fruit often present in some
other plant part such as the bark, resin, seeds or
leaves.

Medicinal fruits

An example of a medicinal IFT species with medicinal qualities in the fruit is the *Zisiphus jujube*.
Called the "red date" in Chinese medicine the small
date—like fruits are prescribed when the body has
been weakened by disease or injury. They are effective against chronic fatigue and encourage the
immune system. Syrup of red dates is soothing for
coughs and irritated throats.

Zisiphus jujube is the best known tree of a medicinally valuable family of trees. *Zisiphus mauritainia*
contains compounds active against skin cancer. *Zisiphus spinochristi* has been used to treat bronchitis
and *Zisiphus micronauta's* hard woody fruit is used
to treat colds and chest problems.

Another example of a family of IFT species that have
medicinal value are the Kiegelias or "sausage fruits."
These trees do indeed produce a fruit that looks very
much like a green sausage. Some species of Kiegelias
are edible if the fruit is gathered and cooked when
the fruit is immature.

But most Kegelias such as *Kiegelia abyssinica* are
valued for their healing properties. *Kiegelia abysin-
ica* is used to make the "muratina brew" reputed to
be a tonic and cure for certain tropical maladies. The
dried powdered fruits *of Kigelia africana* are used to

make an anti eczema cream. Other Kiegelia varieties have anti– biotic and anti bacteria properties and are used to treat ulcers and infected sores.

A third example of medicinal IFT fruit can be found in the Bael tree (Aegle marmelos), The fruit of the bael tree resembles a small withered orange. Like the sweet orange the fruit is high in Vitamin C, has a citrus like coloring and a strongly scented peel. There the resemblance to a sweet orange ends. The fruit of the bael tree is bitter and pungent, growing on a spiny deciduous tree that may reach eight meters in height and considered a laxative, tonic and restorative. Essential oils have been extracted from the leaves twigs and fruit of the tree and are used in other eastern systems of medicine.

While the bael fruit is edible it is not considered ordinary food in the Orient but rather medicine in the form of a fruit.

Medicinal Nuts

IFT species with medicinal nuts are not uncommon. The brazil nut, a rich source of selenium is used to treat depression, infertility in men and proscribed to lower the risk of cancer. The economic importance of this tree in the Amazon basin is second only to that of the rubber tree.

The nut of the *Argania spinosa*, like an almond sealed in an acorn, is pressed into delicious oil that lowers cholesterol in the blood.

The white walnut, a relative of the domesticated walnut Juglans regia, is used to treat skin problems and promote the cleansing of the liver, spleen and gall bladder.

Tea Materials

A list of IFT species that produce leaves and flowers suitable to make tea would be a very long list. There are scores of "tea" plants among the IFT species Teas made from the leaves and flowers of IFT species have been used to treat many health problems and diseases and used to do everything from ridding children of parasitic worms to improving the libido of adults to treating malaria.

The harvest of these types of tea materials, that is leaves flowers and twigs are rarely harmful to the plant.

Minor IFT species such as berries, buckthorns and brambles have become popular as sources of medicinal teas as well. Their leaves and flowers are generally gathered in the spring and summer when the medicinal qualities of the material are at their peak. These materials too can be gathered with little damage to the resource base. (See Figure 23 on page 229.)

Medicinal Bark

The harvest of medicinal bark is problematic. Bark stripped from the trunk regenerates slowly and the scars and wounds left by bark collection may allow insects and disease to attack the tree. If too much bark is taken it can be damaging and even fatal to the tree. The more valuable the material, the more likely that the wild crafter will be tempted to practice unsustainable forms of harvesting that may damage or eliminate the resource entirely.

Some IFT species are in danger of extinction before their evaluation is complete and their domestication has been attempted because their medicinal properties have been recognized before any provisions have been made for their protection.

An example of an endangered IFT species is the Prunus africanus, or Red Stinkwood, a tall evergreen tree with dark cherry—like fruits and white flowers which is found in South Africa and some tropical areas further north.

The bark from the stem is effective in the treatment of hypertension (high blood pressure) and BPH (benign prostate hyperplasia) and harvesting has been so widespread that the tree has been added to the list of endangered medicinal species. This list now includes the above—mentioned Brazil nut, the wild Gingko, the Yerba Mate plant set and several species of yew tree.

When species which produce gum and resin are considered the list of endangered plants becomes much longer, Boswellia serrata (frankincense) Agarwood, Italian cypress, the famous Cedar of Lebanon, the Balm of Gilead tree (Figure 24 on page 229), the Gulgul gum tree and the myrrh are all in danger of extinction in their native ranges, the price perhaps of being too useful to short—sighted humanity.

A relative of Red Sandalwood Santalum fernandi-agum became extinct in 1908, harvested to the last tree for its fragrant wood.

Inherent in medicinal species is a double blessing and a double danger. When a tree or plant is seen only as a source of materia medica and not viewed holistically it is all too easy to justify aggressive and sometimes lethal harvesting techniques, killing the very trees we need to preserve our own health.

On the bright side of the problem medicinal plants are often so useful that they are early candidates for domestication.

The gingko was domesticated thousands of years ago in China because of its medicinal value.

The Cinchona tree from south America, source of quinine, was grown from seed in Java in the nineteenth century in an tempt to domesticate it and break the monopoly some countries had on the precious anti malarial bark. Eventually the tree was domesticated; the monopoly was broken and extensive plantation of Cinchona trees were developed in Indonesia.

Clearly if the medicinal value of IFT species provide an excuse for over utilization and exploitation—then the converse is also true. The same properties may provide the impetus to domesticate, propagate and preserve the species.

Domesticated medicinal trees are for the most part safe. They will survive in orchards, genotype collections and arboretums.

But for the IFT still in the wild, valuable enough to be harvested for medicine but too obscure to warrant protection, *an enforceable program of sustainable harvesting is necessary for species survival.*

Bark can be harvested from wild IFT in strips, patches or pried off the thickened surface at branch divisions, allowing the tree to heal itself between harvesting periods. Bark can be collected from semi—domesticated plants during periods when the plants are pruned.

The supply of medicinal wood can be sometimes increased by coppicing a certain percentage of the trees. Coppicing often encourages the growth of many woody stems.

The best way to promote sustainable harvesting of wild medicinal plants is to grant license and tenure to local wildcrafters and to set a quota on how much materia medica can be harvested from IFT populations.

Licensed and tenured harvesters can be trained in sustainable methods and made to see that it is in their interest to protect the resource base and so insure their own livelihoods.

They are much more likely to take the warning of conservationists seriously than the exploitative and opportunistic wildcrafters who have caused these problems to begin with.

Clear—cutters and tree strippers are after a quick profit and do not care what happens to an area or a species after they have cashed in on whatever they can extract. These are the people who eliminate whole populations of plants and destroy essential forest cover.

Putting them outside the law, as has been done with poachers, is the only way to protect wild medicinal trees.

Conservation

Some plants must be conserved in situ because it is difficult to establish them outside their native range. Now that there is more of a sense in governments that wild animals and wild plants are precious elements of the national commons it is sometimes possible to include IFT rich areas in national parks and preserves.

This means that the mapping of these populations has to be done first and someone, either local environmental activist, concerned researcher of ecologically inclined NGO must lobby for inclusion.

The battle is not won after the IFT rich area becomes part of park. Conservationist regulations regarding animals and plants must be enforced to protect them. This means park rangers or other employees must monitor the population and protect them from poachers and unlicensed extractivists.

Biopiracy

Biopiracy must be discouraged as well by passing strict local laws or taking matters to international courts.

Biopiracy unfortunately, has a history almost as long as agriculture.

For hundreds, even thousands of years certain groups have sought to restrict the planting of various species in order to insure exclusive rights for themselves. This has been especially true in the case of dye materials and spices.

In one particularly horrible example from the 1600's officials of the Dutch East Indian trading company attempted to monopolize the production and sale of cloves. To this end they conquered an island rich in clove trees, destroyed the clove trees on every other island they could find and massacred a goodly percentage of indigenous people who were skilled in its cultivation.

Biopiracy in these days in more likely done in court than on the high seas and on tropical islands.

The Bintagor tree (Callopyllum sp.) of Borneo is an important test case.

The Dayak people of Borneo are a source of considerable indigenous knowledge and tradition concerning this huge relative of the rubber tree. They have used its parts to treat or cure various illnesses and have made a fish—stunning preparation from its poisonous latex.

This tree is also the source of Calanolide A, a possible treatment for AIDS and an experimental anti tuberculosis drug.

The International Convention on Biological Diversity(CBD) went into effect in 1993. The convention was adopted by 179 countries, recognizing the right of each country to regulate the use of its own biological resources.

The state of Sarawak has entered into a joint venture with a company that has investigated the drug and synthesized it, with the intent that 50% of the future profits will return to Sarawak. Other medicinal IFT species are being investigated in hopes of discovering more bio—prospecting bonanzas.

Left undone is the agreement between the state of Sarawak and the local people. What should be a compact t improving the right of the indigenous inhabitants over their own medicinal substances may become just another tool for taking IFT species away from the indigenous as soon as they prove to be valuable in the modern world.

Using the Neem tree as another example—the patents applying to Neem were challenged in court. One patent applied specifically to a substance found in the seeds and the other from a process for extracting and stabilizing the substance. (See Figure 13 on page 225.)

The challenge to the first patent was successful and the patent, which would have limited the use of a natural substance found in the neem seed and kept others from developing neem products was revoked.

This first patent attempted to stymie development of neem products in the countries where the tree originated (and has been used and grown for centuries) and was such a blatant attempt at pirating a biological resource that it raised an international outcry.

The second patent was deemed to be valid because it was a patent for a process that does not interfere with the use of the plant.

From these examples it is clear that it is impossible to protect medicinal IFT species piecemeal. Protection, conservation and use will have to be holistic—this means protecting the trees, the land, the local people who use the species and the local indigenous knowledge.

Chapter Thirteen
Simple Grafting

In the propagation, domestication and development of IFT species grafting could be an extremely useful technique in the effort to bring IFT species into the continuum of use.

Grafting is the art of attaching one piece of living plant tissue to another in such a way that both tissues become united and continue to grow.

The advantage of grafting is in the flexibility it confers on the grafted tree. The grafted tree is made up of tissue from two selected individual trees, one, the rootstock which can be selected for hardiness, tolerances or disease resistance and two, the scion which can then be selected for its characteristics of fruit and yield.

It has become a widely used technique for propagating woody plants that have few seeds and an excellent method for allowing out pollinating species to set fruit.

Grafting has also become a way for tree farmers and plant propagators to clone superior individual trees and so establish new varieties.

And grafting is one of the best ways to extend the areas in which a fruit trees can be planted. This is done by grafting the scions of delicate fruit trees on the rootstocks of hardier relatives or even wild relatives.

Grafting can be a method for improving the yield of existing stands of IFT trees. A wild tree from an IFT species such as the shea butter tree(that germinates from a recalicitrant seed on fallow land and has to survive a long juvenility period before one can discern if the tree has useful fruit and nuts) can be grafted with a scion of a superior tree taking much of the gamble out of raising this IFT species.

Grafted plants are therefore single plants made of the tissues of two or sometimes three plants.

Rootstocks

The plant that supplies the root system for the grafted plant is called the rootstock.

Rootstocks are generally chosen or their hardiness or for specific tolerances such as tolerance to salt, excess iron in the soil, or tolerance to disease and pests. They are usually chosen from species that can be easily propagated by seeds. Seedling rootstocks generally have deeper and more developed root systems than rootstocks made from cuttings. But seeds are variable and if it is necessary for grafted scions to be grafted on exactly the same rootstock for a specific trait or purpose than cuttings of the hardy tree can be used to make rootstocks as well.

Two or three year old plants make good rootstocks as they are still small enough to transplant easily but strong and well established enough to take a graft.

Sometimes the rootstock is a mature tree. Its limbs are cut back and multiple scions are grafted on the stem. This is called **topworking** and allows a skilled orcharder to replace a strong but undesirable tree with a more useful cultivar.

The Influence of the Rootstock

A rootstock can influence a scion in many ways. Scions will develop into very small trees if grafted on a rootstock that has dwarfing qualities. Fruit of various citruses will develop smooth peels or ridged and bumpy peels depending on which rootstock has been used when the trees were grafted.

Rootstocks can protect the scion from disease or poor soil conditions. The black walnut for instance is resistant to a disease that attacks the root system of the edible English walnut. Grafting an English walnut scion on its stronger and more adapted wild relative produces a hardy tree.

Mangoes grafted on rootstocks with tolerances to high ph allow the trees to be cultivated in alkaline soil.

Both the rootstock and the scion should be of closely related species and therefore physiologically similar.

Most apples scions can be grafted on crab apple stock. Most citrus scions can be grafted on the bitter orange or the coarse lemon.

Occasionally it is possible to cross graft between fruiting plants in the same genus—for instance grafting pears on quince stock or tomato on potato.

Incompatibility

There are varieties within the same species that cannot be grafted to one another. When this happens it is said that the scion and rootstock are **incompatible**.

Incompatibility between rootstock and scion can occur if either plant part is infected with a bacterial disease or a virus.

It can also occur due to simple differences in physiology.

Some grafts appear to take but there is a general failure to thrive in the scion. There may be slow healing of the scar of the union, lack of vigor in the plant, symptoms of dieback in the branches. In some cases the rootstock will grow much thicker than the scion, bulging like a bottle, and begin to put up suckers.

In this case it is best to cut back the stock and discard the scion. If the stock survives it may be grafted again more successfully.

Scions

Scions are the upper part of the graft, usually chosen because of their useful fruits, nuts or other product. Scions are grafted on rootstocks to make it easier for them to survive or simply to propagate them— because grafting a scion on a rootstock is a much faster and more reliable process than trying to grow tree similar to the scion from seed.

Generally scions are one year old stem pieces 5 to 12 cm long and one fourth to one cm in diameter carrying several buds. It is important that there be leaf buds as well as flower buds on a scion. Leaf buds are often shaped differently than flower buds, narrow and pointed while the flower buds have round shapes.

Scions for grafting deciduous trees are collected while the tree is dormant.

Scion material should be collected from the middle of the branches because branch tips are often low in stored nutrients and the bases of dormant branches are often deficient in buds. Scions and rootstock should be the same diameter for many simple grafts.

The grafting may be done in early spring for trees that are dormant and the graft protected by wax, tape or grafting tar.

If the graft is successful the grafted branch will leaf out at the same time the stock does.

Scions for evergreen trees should be chosen from last year's shoots. The stem of these shoots should be green and healthy and the base of the scion should be only slightly less in thickness than the diameter of the rootstock.

Grafting for evergreen trees is more successful if done in early spring or in the autumn. Evergreeen scions may wilt or freeze if grafting is attempted in the extremes of the year.

Bridge grafts

Sometimes a scion is not compatible with a rootstock and a bridge graft is made. First the bridge tissue called the interstem is grafted on the rootstock. After the graft scar heals and the interstem has put out new leaves the scion is grafted onto it. Needless to say the interstem has to be compatible with both rootstock and scion.

The process of grafting

The aim of grafting is to join the cambium—the active green layer under the bark—of the rootstock and the scion. If properly fitted together the cambium of the two parts produces wound tissue, called callus. When the two callussed areas grow together and the cells intermingle some of the callus cells develop into cambium cells which unite the rootstock and the scion. Once there is a continuous connection between the two cambium layers the graft is complete.

Grafting must be practiced to achieve good results. Clean flat grafting cuts done with a sharp knife insure maximum contact between the two cambium layers. Grafting should be done quickly so the surface do not dry out.

Rootstocks and scions of the same diameter insure maximum contact. If much larger rootstocks are used side grafts or veneer grafts insure that one side of the cambium layer o f the scion is properly fitted to the cambium of the bigger rootstock.

Besides a sharp knife a clean, sharp pair of pruning shears is useful for cutting back rootstock tops and collecting scions. Grafting tapes or ties are also necessary to hold the scions and rootstocks together until callus can form. Rubber bands, waxed string, masking tape or electrical tape are all suitable for grafting.

Grafting ties should overlap slightly as they are wrapped about the union, covering both stems for an inch in either direction of the graft.

Grafting waxes can be used with grafting ties to hold the scion in place and protect the union from disease organisms, drying out, weather events, insects and excess moisture.

Commercial tree paint is also suitable for use in protecting new grafts though the paint should be reapplied if rain falls within a day of the graft.

Check wrapped grafts after month to see if the union has occurred.

If the graft has been successful the scion will be alive perhaps even leafing out.

If the graft scar has healed it is possible to cut the graft ties.

If healing is incomplete the graft can be rewrapped and checked again later in the season. The ties must be cut away from a successful graft so they do not girdle the stem of the scion, which will grow rapidly when the union is complete.

Planting grafted trees

When grafted trees are planted out the union should be above soil level to minimize the danger of fungus organisms attacking the graft. Scions may form their own roots if the union is too close to the soil which is not a bad thing unless the rootstock has been chosen for an influential trait, such a dwarfing rootstock.

Rootstocks should not be allowed to form suckers(shoots from the rootstock). Powerful suckers from the rootstock can crowd out or kill a weak scion.

Check grafted plants several times a season. When scions grow tall they should be supported or cut back so they will not be prone to breaking.

When and why might grafting be used in the development of IFT

IFT as rootstocks.

IFT species with cultivated relatives are natural candidates for rootstocks. While much trail and error experimentation must take place before the mango is grafted on the marula (both trees from the family of Anacardiacae) the tolerances, resistances and well—developed root systems of the wild trees can be used to protect and invigorate their cultivated relatives.

Some IFT species are already being used in this matter such as the black walnut and the crab apple.

Systematic investigation will produce many more wild and cultivated pairings that will allow the cultivated trees to fight disease and survive in challenging conditions.

IFT as scions

As IFT species are investigated the great variability of product size, color and value will prompt a more standardized way of propagation simply so the more useful types of tree may be distributed to farmers and researchers.

In these cases the rootstock and the scions will be of the same IFT species. The rootstocks will simply be vigorous local seedlings and the scions will be types selected for their useful characteristics and traits.

Grafting a branch of a good pollinator on an out pollinating IFT tree is a useful technique as are transsexual grafts for the dioecious IFT species.

Suggested grafting techniques for IFT

Since there is little information about incompatibility or other possible problems in IFT species simpler methods of grafting should be attempted first.

Head grafts

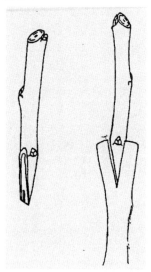

Head grafts are the simplest form of grafting. Both scion and rootstock are approximately the same size. The rootstock is cut back with a straight cut and split about five centimeters down the from cut. The scion is shaped like an elongated v and clipped in the split for maximum contact of the cambium layers.

Whip and Tongue Grafts

Whip and Tongue Grafts are particularly useful for grafting relatively small plant materials from about. 5 cm to 1 cm in diameter. This graft heals quickly with good contact surfaces between the graft and the cambium making a strong union.

Stock and scion should be approximately the same diameter.

The scion should carry at least three buds. And the graft should be made in the internode below the lower bud.

It is extremely important that the cambium layer match perfectly at least along one side and that the lower edge of the scion should not overhang the stock. Scions larger in diameter than rootstocks should be avoided when using this grafting technique. Scions smaller in diameter should be fitted carefully long one side for maximum contact. This graft should be tied and covered until the union is completely healed over.

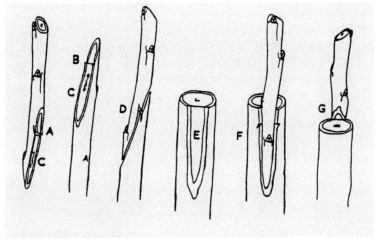

Whip and Tongue Grafting
A and B : the notched scion fits into the matching notched stock (C and D)

Splice Granting and Stub Grafting
E: a single slanting cut in the stock
F: a cut of the same angle and length in the scion
G: scion and stock are fitted together

This drawing is a reprint from the book The Propagation of Tropical Fruit Trees by Garner and Chaundhri, FAO, CAB, 1988)

Splice Grafting

This method of grafting is useful in grafting plants that have a pithy stem or wood which is too inflexible to permit a tight fit when a tongue is made and tends to split too far and too easily during for a head graft.

A single slanting cut in made of the same length and same angle in both stock and scion in the following manner: The cut is made one third to one half way through the stem of the stock, this can be done with a grafting knife or a small chisel. The base of the scion is cut to a thin wedge. The top of the stock branch is pulled back. The scion is inserted in this cut angled slightly to the side for maximum contact of cambium layers. The stock is cut off just above the scion. The union is bound and waxed.

Stub Grafting

Stub grafting, done on larger branches and very useful when dealing with trees with very hard wood is accomplished in a similar manner.

Side Tongue Grafts

Side tongue grafts are useful for small evergreen plant material. On the stock a piece of wood and bark is removed about a quarter way through the stem. A second downward cut is made forming a thin tongue. The scion is prepared in a similar

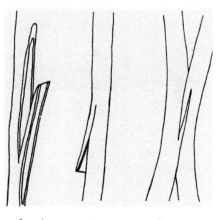

manner with one long sloping put across the base and a similar cut under the first forming a tongue. The scion is then slipped into the stock, the two tongues interlocking and the cambium layers matching along one side. The graft is tied and waxed. The top of the stock is not removed until the union is healed.

Side Veneer Grafting

Side veneer grafting is a method used for bushes and small evergreen plants. A shallow downward and inward cut is made on the stock about 2.5 to 3 cm long just below the crown of the stock. At the base of the cut a straight cut is made which intersects the first, allowing a section of wood and bark to be removed. The scion is shaped with a long downward but and a short basal one and fits in the area where the wood and bark section of the rootstock was removed. The graft is tightly wrapped and put under glass or in a greenhouse or mist chamber for a moister more protective environment since the scion is not cut back and may wilt and die before union.

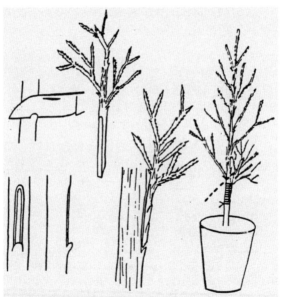

This drawing is a reprint from the book The Propagation of Tropical Fruit Trees by Garner and Chaundhri, FAO, CAB, 1988)

Cleft Grafting

Cleft grafting is a useful method in grafting and top-working larger and older plant material with stocks from 2. 5 to 10 cm in diameter. It is particularly effective on plants with a dormancy period and is most successful in the early spring when buds of the stock are just beginning to swell but active plant growth has not yet started. The stocks can be mature and large branches but the scions should be of year old wood.

In sawing off the stock the cut should be made at right angles to the main axis of the branch. A heavy knife can be used to make a vertical split 5 to 8 cm down the center of the stub to be grafted. Two scions are inserted one at each side of the cleft, they should be from 7 to 11 cm in length, shaped into wedges at the base and carry three or more buds. Their outside edge should be slightly thicker than their inner edge.

Since the bark of the stock is thicker than the bark of the scion the scions should be set slightly in for maximum contact. This kind of graft must be closed completely with wax or other materials such as tree paint or tar.

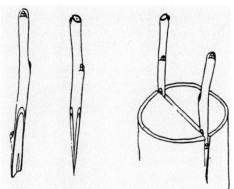

This drawing is a reprint from the book The Propagation of Tropical Fruit Trees by Garner and Chaundhri, FAO, CAB, 1988)

Bud Grafting.

There are several methods for grafting not a branch of piece of stem but a single bud. Bud grafts are less of a strain on the stock and the graft wounds generally heal quickly. There is little chance of the stock breaking and a grafted bud can develop almost as rapidly as a granted branch. Bud grafting should be considered as a grafting method for challenging environments.

See the drawing below for the most common method.

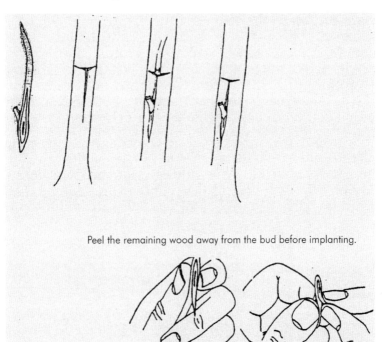

Peel the remaining wood away from the bud before implanting.

This drawing is a reprint from the book The Propagation of Tropical Fruit Trees by Garner and Chaundhri, FAO, CAB, 1988)

In short grafting of IFT species is another way to ensure quality and quantity of fruit, to give some control to the farmer or researcher over where and when IFT species are planted, to extend ranges and propagate hardy plants and to allow for good fruit set in the absence of compatible pollinating partners.

Grafting is therefore another important tool in the development and domestication of IFT as crop candidates and alternative crops.

Chapter Fourteen
Simple Propagation

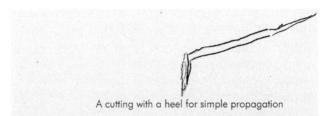

A cutting with a heel for simple propagation

A: Plant bent to the ground for simple layering
B: The plant is staked to the earth with wire and pegs (D)
C: shoots grow up from the staked plant and earth heaped up to encourage root development

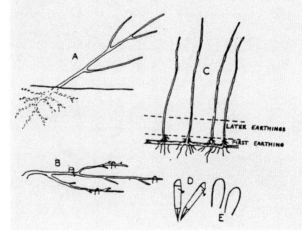

Propagating IFT

Learning to propagate plants, making new plants from existing ones, is a necessary skill for work with IFT.

Establishing an experimental plot may require that IFT species be started from seed or made from stem cuttings of trees in the wild.

IFT species may need to be taken to another location for study and propagated for this purpose from suckers or root cuttings.

Many IFT species have specialized propagules such as offshoots, bulblets, offsets, burls or divisions that a farmer or researcher could use advantageously.

Since so little information is available about IFT species the farmer, researcher or collector might have to create an appropriate propagation protocol for the plants he is interested in.

Some day IFT species may be created and sold in commercial plant nurseries in the manner of roses and apple trees. But today with the exception of a few IFT which have been propagated as ornamental plants, a person who wants to work with IFT will most likely have to make his or her own plants.

Fortunately most propagation methods are easy and cheap and do not need special conditions or expensive tools.

Sexual reproduction

Propagation from seeds: Growing IFT from seeds is an inexpensive way to produce large numbers of plants. Raising seeds requires few materials. Seedlings can be raised in plain earth, compost or potting mixture in any handy container that allows for drainage. Paper cups, tin cans, sawed—off plastic bottles and many other discarded containers that can be picked out of modern trash heaps make perfectly adequate pots. Apart from the seeds, the medium and the container only water and patience are needed to produce as many plants as the IFT enthusiast might want.

The exception of course are recalcitrant seeds which will be discussed in the next chapter (Chapter 15)

But the plants raised from seed will be variable in all their characteristics just as the seeds are.

They are the products of sexual reproduction and the fusion of the male and female reproductive cells.

If a plant just like the parent plant is desired than some sort of asexual reproduction will have to be done.

Asexual reproduction methods use the vegetative parts of the plant—roots, stems and leaves to make a new plant exactly like the parent plant. A plant produced from one of these parts or from a specialized plant propagule is basically a clone of the parent plant and will have the characteristics of the parent plant.

Divisions: Division is an easy way to propagate plants with multiple stems or trunks, especially if the plants have a dormancy period. One side of the established plant may be dug up and a stem or trunk with a good piece of root attached may be removed and potted or transplanted to the desired location. A few examples of IFT species that may be propagated in this manner are Zisiphus jujube, hawthorns, most species of bamboo and many berries and brambles.

Suckers and root cuttings: Since many IFT species have single trunks or stems and division is not possible, suckers from the roots of established plants, though slower to grow than divisions, are an effective way to propagate established plants without doing damage.

These new stems or suckers usually come up relatively close to the trunk of the parent tree. They are also natural clones of the parent plant. Suckers can be dug up and separated from the parent plant with a goodly piece of root attached and potted or transplanted to another location.

Cuttings: Stem and leaf cuttings are separated from the parent plant and placed in conditions that facilitate the formation of new roots and shoots. During this process they need a medium to support them and a structure to protect them from weather, temperatures and water loss. The best media for cuttings of this type are sterile, water retentive but well drained materials such as perlite, vermiculite, baked compost or peat.

Cuttings can be rooted in soil or sand but there is always a danger of contamination or attack from fungi and other organisms on the vulnerable cut surface.

Cuttings should be made with a clean sharp tool such as a box cutter or a scissors type pruning shears.

Cuttings should contain at least two buds but usually do well if they are slightly longer. Eight to twelve centimeter cuttings are good for most plants and they should be taken from healthy plants that are not flowering or in fruit.

Never propagate plants infested by insects, discolored plants, plants that are yellowed or plants that have recently been sprayed.

The containers use to receive the cuttings should be scrubbed clean and steamed or rinsed in a weak solution of bleach (approximately 8%) If there are large numbers of cuttings to be planted this can be done in wooden or plastic flats. These flats can be scrubbed and steamed just as flowerpots or other containers though it is not recommended to use bleaching solutions on wooden flats.

Rooting hormones can encourage root formation on stem cuttings of hard to root plants and speed root development of other plants. Commercial rooting hormone powders are available from plant nurseries and by mail from the Internet. Read labels and descriptions carefully because some rooting hormones contain fungicides.

A home made solution known as willow water can also encourage your cuttings to root. It is prepared by cutting willow stems (Salix) into small pieces and soaking these pieces in warm water in a covered container for 24 hours. Strain the willow water into a clean bucket and soak cuttings in it overnight before planting.

Cuttings need a protected, high humidity environment while they are developing roots. If the surrounding air is moist there is minimal water loss and this helps the cutting survive until the roots grow.

A small green house is useful when propagating plants from cuttings. One can be improvised from a sturdy framework and nylon film. A cold frame or cloche also makes a good structure for rooting cuttings

Or a plastic bag can be taped over an individual pot of cuttings on sticks wires or some other support. As long as the plastic does not touch the cuttings and the bag is opened for an hour every day the moisture will be kept in effectively and give the cuttings a chance to develop.

To harden off cuttings rooted in this manner expose the pots to the air for longer periods each day.

Soil warmth encourages roots to develop, electric soil warmers and hot mattresses are available by mail from most nursery firms but this type of equipment can also be improvised from blind drip irrigation pipe and a solar powered hot water heater.

Flats of cuttings can be placed over a radiator or on top of a refrigerator. To see whether or not roots are forming it is best to look at the bottom of the container, do not pull on the cuttings or disturb the upper layers of soil in which they are planted.

Hardwood cuttings will root more readily if taken during the dormancy period of the parent plant. Take the cuttings after leaf fall but before the renewal of growth in the spring. Late autumn and early winter is a good time to plant these cuttings so they have adequate time to form roots before the buds begin to grow. Hardwood cuttings do not generally need conditions of high humidity in their dormant state Most deciduous or semi deciduous trees can be rooted in this manner as well as vines and many berries.

Softwood cuttings should be taken from spring growth. Make sure the cuttings contain a terminal bud. These cutting form roots rapidly but are delicate and do need conditions of high humidity, good sanitation and warmth to root successfully. After the cuttings have rooted good ventilation and a gradual hardening off are advised. Rooted softwood cuttings should be planted out before the full heat of summer in a cool and protected place.

Evergreen cuttings: Broad—leaved and needled evergreen trees can also be propagated by stem cuttings. Broad—leaved cuttings should be taken in late summer from year old shoots, sometimes an older piece of wood, called a heel. (See page 126.) left at the base of the stem is helpful in getting good root development To make a heel pull the branch down sharply, pulling away a piece of stem from the parent plant. Trim off excess tissue with a knife or shears.

Heels on cuttings also help when rooting needled evergreens. These cuttings should be collected in the autumn or winter. Well—drained rooting medium is a must for evergreen cuttings. Before planting remove lower leaves and side shoots to make a bare stem. Plant the cuttings about one third of the length in the rooting medium. Ventilate and water carefully until rooted cuttings are hardened off.

Simple layering and air layering: Layering is a technique used to induce plant stems to root while still attached to the parent plant. Some plants produce layers naturally such as strawberries that form new plants on runners that spread out from the parent plant. Blackberries and raspberries make new plants where the tips of the canes touch the ground. Plants of spreading habit may form roots if plant stems are covered along any part of their length with earth.

To encourage this process bend a low growing stem of a plant to the ground and bury in the earth. Sometimes it is necessary to wound or kink the stem to encourage the stem to produce roots. (See page 126.)

Air layering is done with erect stems that are less flexible or too high on the parent plant to be bent to the ground. A suitable rooting media is secured to a plant stem after it has been shallowly wounded twelve cm to forty cm below the growing tip. This wound can be dusted with rooting hormone to speed the process. The medium is usually held in place by a sheet of plastic or tough nylon film and tied or rubber banded in place around the stem on both sides of the cut. It is important that these ends be tightly

closed to keep moisture in the medium. The resulting bulge can be covered with aluminum foil to protect the layered area from overheating. When roots
are visible through the plastic the stem can be
clipped below the medium and the new plant potted
or planted out.

Offshoots: Offshoots are perfect natural clones of the
parent plant. Many palms produce offshoots but offshoots grace a good many useful plants and they can
usually be removed easily and then potted or planted
on their own.

If an offshoot is growing near the ground or below
ground level there is a good possibility that it already
has an independent root system. If this is the case
the offshoot can be separated from the parent plant.

Offshoots that grow out above the ground usually do
not have enough roots to survive independently. The
base of the offshoot can be bagged and filled with
moss or sawdust in a manner very like air layering.
If this material is kept moist many new roots will
form and the offshoot can be removed.

The connection between the parent plant and the
offshoot may be as tenuous as a few roots or as firm
as a woody cable. The IFT farmer or researcher
should dig away the earth from an offshoot and
determine what kind of connection exists between
offshoot and parent In the case of some palms such
as the date palm the connection has to be severed
with a large headed chisel and hammer or a powered
saw.

Burls: Burls are basically masses of plant tissue usually close to the root zone of specific plants. Burls are
capable of putting forth shoots and roots in the right
conditions. A burl that has roots and shoots but is
still attached to the parent plant can be removed to
produce an independent plant much in the way that

offshoots can be removed. Trees growing in moist climate or rooting in water often develop burls. (See Figure 25 on page 230.)

So little is known about IFT species that a certain amount of experimentation will be needed to find the most effective way to propagate specific species.

But like grafting simple propagation of the species is a necessary step to their domestication and development.

Chapter Fifteen
Interdependent Horticultural Problems

Propagating IFT species is not always as simple as putting a seed in the ground or taking a cutting and then raising a tree to maturity.

Sometimes there are very good reasons why a species has remained a wild crop, such as characteristics of seed, fruit, or plant development that are true obstacles to domestication and utilization.

For example, recalcitrant seed makes planting and propagating IFT a much more complicated process. Time and effort must be expanded to find out how to germinate the seed and keep the young plant alive so that seedlings and later saplings can be produced when needed for planting.

A seed that is viable for only days or weeks is also a problem but a problem of a different sort. This IFT plant can only be propagated if the seed is fresh. There will be a wait of an fruiting season, perhaps a year, if the proper time for planting that seed is missed.

A good example of a common tree with a very short seed viability period is the medicinal Neem tree native to India. Seeds planted six weeks after they fall from the tree rarely sprout.

There are also IFT seeds that must be scarified or soaked to remove growth inhibitors or require exposure to extremes of temperature before they can germinate.

The seeds of the Quondong tree are very difficult to sprout and even when treated may not germinate for years. (See Figure 14 on page 226.)

There are IFT species that germinate only in extreme environments, and others that will not sprout unless they pass through the digestive system of a bird or mammal.

After an IFT seed has been sprouted there are other possible obstacles to domestication and utilization. Some species cannot be grafted or propagated by cuttings and so will not fit into cultivated formats. Other species are dependent on soil symbionts or companion organisms and will not thrive or germinate without them.

Out breeding is another possible obstacle because a suitable pollination partner must be supplied for each tree and often the insect vectors must be discovered and introduced to an IFT test site or new planting as well.

But the case of the shea butter tree is special even among the more difficult to domesticate African IFT species. This species has not one obstacle to development but an intertwined knot of horticultural problems that keep it from fully entering a state of domestication and keep it on the fringes of the agricultural world.

The Case of the Shea Butter Tree.

Background information: The shea butter tree, the source of kararite, is an important source of income and nutrition for rural people in a broad belt of Africa from Senegal through the Sahel. The tree's importance as a food source is due to the oil in the kernel, which allows for the production of "shea butter" and excellent vegetable fat. Other uses in the household are cheese making, soap manufacture, cosmetic oil, and oil for illumination. *V. paradoxa* is the dominant species in savanna parklands, vast managed ecosystems which pass through alternating states of cultivation and fallow.

Unfortunately, pressure from hungry and landless populations have shortened the traditional fallow periods and most *V. paradoxa* stands are aging and thinning. Improving the yield and quality of shea butter trees and introducing improved types into new cultivation cycles could significantly enhance the role of the shea butter tree as a cash crop and a source of food, as well as preserving the genetic diversity of the species.

While much is known in Africa about the cultivation, harvesting, and use of the fruits and the production of shea butter, very little has been done about improving the plants or protecting the genetic diversity of the species or restoring the balance of the existing stands of trees. *V. pardoxa* is an undervalued and underutilized crop, despite its importance to rural people in a vast area of the African continent, one that could be improved quickly and commercialized to some extent in order to increase opportunities for producing edible and useful shea products, bring employment options and much needed money to impoverished local economies. As a trade commodity Shea butter has a long history in West Africa. The oil has been traded extensively for the last five hundred years as well as the medicinal bark and the extremely hard wood that is often used to make furniture and mortars.

The Vitellaria is also a source of charcoal and glue—like latex used in local crafts.

Managing stands of Vitellaria by selective clearing and integrating shea trees into sorghum, millet and yam based farming systems are two of the traditional approaches to the cultivation of the shea tree.

V. paradoxa has been a major component of African agroforestry systems for many years as the tree is highly valued because of the oil extracted from its dried kernels, its nutritious fruit, its valuable timber and medicinal bark. The oil is the main oleaginous product in many areas of this species semi arid range. It is widely utilized for purposes such as cooking, as skin moisturizer or as an illuminant. Shea butter is also sold as an ingredient in cosmetic, pharmaceutical and edible products bringing in needed cash to local economies.

The shea trees are an inclusion in the long cycle "gum garden" rotation of the more arid areas in the species range in which the shea tree is planted as the regenerative phase of the rotation, tapped for latex in the trees juvenility period, utilized for fruit and oil for two to three decades then felled and burned to enrich the soil before the vegetable and grain phase of the rotation.

Stands of the tree are often tended by local farmers who eliminate unwanted woody species and leave the shea trees to grow. Selection during land clearance based on criteria that include spacing, health and yield has resulted in the development what can be considered landraces despite the status of the shea as a wild tree.

At the fourth session of the FAO panel on African forest genetic resources in 1977 the Vitellaria tree was recognized as one of the most important underutilized IFT species in Africa. In 1984 and 1988 FAO panels recommended botanical and genetic exploration, as well provenance trails with an eye to tree improvement. In 1986 a research program into diversity, management and shea butter tree propagation was started.

It was recommended at the sixth session of the FAO panel in 1999 that a greater understanding of the life cycle of the shea butter tree and its place in the farming ecosystem must be achieved as well as the documentation of the effect of modern agricultural techniques on yield, sustainability and viability of the crop.

Mapping genetic resources.

Attempts were made in several African countries to identify the centers of biodiversity for the Vitellaria population and catalogue the genetic variability of its emerging landraces Tree leaf and seed size measurements were recorded in many sites and conservation strategies were formulated. The Vitellaria species proved to be extremely variable as to seed size, tree height and diameter, fruit size, leaf and petiole color. While there is a small positive relationship between tree size and seed size no relationship has been found between seed size and seed fat content, or the morphological characteristics of the tree and its value as a productive plant. Environmental factors also influence tree morphology, seed size and fruit quality with distinct types develop under different conditions with tall straight boled high canopy trees growing in areas with more rainfall and spreading short boled trees in areas with less water and fewer competing species. (PN Lovett and N Haq (1999).

Since there is little correlation between the different types or landraces morphology and the worth of the individual trees in these groups as crop plants it has become apparent that improvement of the Vitellaria pardoxa as a crop is going to depend on searching for and finding exceptional individual trees. These trees will be chosen for specific sets of characteristics relating to the yield and quality of their fruit, the percentage and quality of oil in their kernels and their general hardiness in areas where shea butter tree cultivation is or was important.

This will mean looking closely at local genetic resources and investigating *V. paradoxa*'s sister species *V. nilotica*.

Local knowledge in the shea tree's range is extensive with 88% percent of farmers interviewed knowing where the best and the most productive trees are found (Lovett and Haq). This information will be crucial to a program of tree improvement as superior trees will be sought out for propagation.

40 percent of the farmers described the topographic situation as most important influence regarding the quality of the trees primary products and suggesting that the best trees are found on higher land.

28 percent of the farmers said that companion vegetation and soil type are also important influences will the best individuals found on cultivated land with well—drained stony and loamy soils.

The Benefits of Improving the Crop

The improvement of *V. paradoxa* will lead to an increase in yield and fruit quality, disease tolerance and general hardiness of the trees, making *V. paradoxa* more valuable and insuring that more trees remain in traditional cultivation/fallow cycles

Modern evaluation and propagation techniques added to local traditional knowledge and methods could help preserve the great tradition of V. paradoxa cultivation while increasing yields, helping in the regeneration of the stands of trees, and bringing more income to the rural people.

V. paradoxa can also be examined as a crop candidate for other countries.

But many obstacles stand between the shea nut tree and its full potential as a crop for arid lands including seed recalcitrance, a long juvenility period, random germination of trees, out—pollinating and a productive population tied to long term fallows and long term crop cycles.

These are obstacles to the shea trees domestication that are most likely responsible for the fact that the sheanut tree is still considered to be wild despite being widely used and integrated into local farming systems for centuries.

These characteristics make tree improvement through simple methodical selection a very complicated laborious process.

However superior individual plants exist on farmland where they have been evaluated by the farmers and included deliberately because of the quality of their products.

Included trees are generally trees with sweet fruit as well as good health, high yield and high percentage of oil from the kernels. Other valued characteristics are low levels of competitive effects on integrated crops, fast growth and resistance to mistletoe parasites.

This type of selection by farmers, balancing crop productivity and tree productivity has resulted in a balance between total woody biomass and crop biomass in integrated plantings.

Unwanted mature trees are killed by ring barking and allowed to dry before being harvested for household uses.

Since the farmland population does not regenerate in situ the new trees are selected from fallows, lands that have been deliberately excluded from cultivation for five to 15 years. Shea experts P. Lovett and N. Haq describe this process in their paper *"Evidence for Anthopic Selection of the Sheanut tree"* published in 2000 by Kluwer Publishers.

New trees for farmland Sheanut populations are selected by not cutting them down with unwanted woody species and protecting them from fire during the cyclical clearing of fallow land

Regeneration of the shea stands therefore takes place only on fallow land as there the fallen seeds can germinate and the young trees can pass their relatively long juvenility period.

Population pressure and the demand for land for more immediate crop benefits has eliminated much fallow land so in many areas the shea stands are thinning and aging and not being replaced.

The shea farmer cannot plant trees where he would like but must depend on the germination of an exceedingly recalcitrant seed in fallow areas. The shea farmer cannot control the quality and productivity of the trees that do germinate but only cull trees that are unproductive. The long juvenility period of the shea precludes irrigation, composting or other investments of time and inputs since the usefulness of the tree will only be established as it reaches maturity. While superior individual trees have been identified there have been no organized attempts to improving the shea crop by organized collection, cultivation and evaluation and selection.

Problem 1: Seed Recalcitrance

The first of the problems that must be addressed is seed recalcitrance. Shea trees only regenerate on fallow land because seed germination is a lengthy and uncertain process probably due to the presence in the seed of growth inhibitors, a characteristic of many plants from arid and semi arid areas. As fallow land becomes less available the shea population must inevitably decline unless a way is found to germinate the seeds whenever required in local nurseries and research facilities.

The extreme randomness of natural regeneration precludes the development of orchard formats, complicates crop improvement by selection, and discourages investment of inputs by the shea farmer. Seeds germinate where they have fallen, a process that may take several years. It is not known if the seedling tree that does come up will be productive until the tree reaches maturity. Therefore shea trees cannot be properly spaced or planted in areas especially favorable for shea cultivation though shea farmers express an almost universal preference for shea trees that grow on higher well—drained soil.

Finding the solutions: Seed recalcitrance must be overcome and control over the germination of the shea nut must be established before any selection and propagation of seedling trees can happen.

Seed recalcitrance can be challenged by physical means such as nicking, scarring, drilling, sanding to thin the shell, soaking in hot water, ingestion by a ruminant before planting. The seeds will be examined for hidden operculi, they can be cracked, whole embryo extraction attempted. Seed recalcitrance can be challenged by chemical means: seeds can be soaked in mild acid, enzymatic fertilizer, placed in warm compost piles or fresh manure and guano.

Seed recalcitrance can also be challenged by soaking in gibberelic acid and rooting hormones.

Seedling trees will be important to the program of tree improvement as genotypes and needed for as rootstocks for grafting experiments so finding the answer to the problem of seed recalcitrance will be a positive first development.

Problem 2: The Long Juvenility Period

The second problem is the long juvenility period of the seedling tree. No farmer can allow himself to invest fertilizer, water and labor for 12 to 20 years in trees that might not be productive. So young shea trees are not pruned, not top—dressed with compost and manure and never irrigated. The end result is that many shea trees that do not produce sufficiently valuable fruits and nuts are culled for firewood, charcoal or lumber. On the other hand productive trees have been starved of needed nutrients and attention and so are never as strong and productive as they might have been. 12 to 20 years may pass while the tree continues to grow with no appreciable yield or benefit until the tree begins to bear fruit and can be evaluated by the farmer. This period of uncertainty coupled with the fact that sheanut trees come up where seeds spout and can not be planted in areas particularly suited to the cultivation of the tree is a true obstacle to the domestication and utilization of the species.

The juvenility period of the tree must be turned from a disadvantage to an advantage. This can be done by grafting the scions of trees of excellent quality on young trees coming up in fallow lands. A fifteen—year old tree, top—worked with scions of a productive tree will fruit very quickly and begin to produce fruits and kernels and soon justify the farmers' investment. The problem of out pollination will also be solved as scions of compatible tree can be grafted on a tree in need of pollination or on a neighboring previously non compatible tree. A two—pronged effort will be needed to surmount this obstacles. The development of grafting techniques will allow a shea farmer to topwork trees that are advantageously placed but of uncertain fruiting quality. Cloning and deliberate planting of the best shea trees will take much of the gamble out of shea cultivation allowing for the establishment of stands of shea trees exactly where the farmer wants them in numbers which can be supported by the farm.

The juvenility period will be shortened to allow for the establishment of groves and orchards of trees propagated by cuttings. Scions of superior trees grafted on seedling trees, tended and pruned in nursery formats have reduced the juvenility period of many fruit and nut trees including the pistachio and the quandong (Santalum acuminatum), trees that have very long juvenility periods in the wild as well as recalcitrant seeds. Cloned trees, ungrafted but propagated from the most productive fruiting stocks have juvenility periods approaching those of most conventional cultivars. Similar treatments of shea germplasm may reduce the juvenility period by many years and therefore make the shea tree more competitive with tree crops that can be harvested quickly.

Other possible ways to shorten the juvenility period:

Drip irrigation of trees in the dry season may considerably shorten juvenility periods as the growth of the shea tree stops when water is scarce. In extreme heat and dryness the tree will shed leaves, enter a dormancy period or die.

Periodic drip irrigation during the dry season allows for steady and quicker development.

Top dressing with local manure or compost also aids the tree in its steady growth toward maturity. Now shea trees are not given compost or manure as it is not known if they will be productive trees until after flowering and fruiting. If it was known that a productive tree would be stronger and a better producer because of these efforts the investment in manure and compost would be logical. There would be more incentive to use drip irrigation too if farmers were sure of some return on a plant.

Pruning and shaping shea trees in the manner of conventional cultivated orchard trees may also contribute to earlier maturity. This has been the case with another IFT species with a recalcitrant seed, the marula, which when topped and shaped begins to fruit in its fourth year while unpruned saplings do not fruit until they are several years older.

Another possibility worthy of examination is inducing the shea trees to flower by applying enzymatic or foliar fertilizers.

But the introduction of saplings propagated from superior individual trees holds the most potential for swift and substantial gains in yield and quality of fruits and kernels

Problem 3: Getting Varietal Plant Material into the Shea Grove

Little work has been done to identify and breed for shea nut varieties.

12 to 20 years may pass before the tree begins to bear fruit and can be evaluated by the farmer. This period of uncertainty coupled with the fact that sheanut trees come up where seeds spout and can not be planted in areas particularly suited to the cultivation of the tree is a true obstacle to the domestication and utilization of the species. Sapling trees, propagated from cuttings or tissue of exceptional individual tree that are already included in farming

systems can be distributed to shea to replace poor quality germplasm

With the certainty of better yield and quality of both fruits and kernel shea cultivation will be more profitable and easier to do.

The development of grafting techniques will allow a shea farmer to topwork trees that are advantageously placed but of uncertain fruiting quality. Cloning and deliberate planting of the best shea trees will take much of the gamble out of shea cultivation allowing for the establishment of stands of shea trees exactly where the farmer wants them in numbers which can be supported by the farm.

The *V. paradoxa* tree might be improved quickly by various horticultural methods such as tissue culture, top working, grafting and selection, thereby encouraging local populations to continue to allocate land to the shea in the regenerative phase of crop rotation and to preserve existing stands. Improvement will also initiate the practice of planting superior trees deliberately in areas especially suitable for shea cultivation rather than depending on the random renewal of shea resources from fallow lands.

Problem 4: Randomness of Renewal

A farmer cannot at this time plant a shea orchard or grove where one is wanted or needed but only wait to see what comes up in fallowed land.

The shea tree currently cannot be planted, it must so to speak, plant itself

This precludes the deliberate introduction of shea orchards, the use of the shea nut tree in agroforestry, as well as complicates the improvement of the crop by selection and breeding of superior trees from generation to generation.

Indeed, each shea farmer starts over from scratch in fallow land with each generation of young shea plants

African farmers still consider the shea tree to be a wild species with good reason.

This extreme randomness has been very detrimental to the shea's development. There is no continuity between the trees of yesterday, the trees of today and the trees of tomorrow.

A farmer may have a fine tree on his property, productive with fruits and kernels of excellent quality. But there is no way to preserve this plant for future planting or plant a tree like it in another place.

The process of crop improvement by selection cannot be effective until there is some control over where trees are planted and less of a gamble on their usefulness and the quality of their products.

The three previous problems and their solutions have great bearing on this matter.

Solving the problem of seed recalcitrance and by mastering grafting and vegetative propagation gives the shea farmer some control as to where he will grow his trees and which trees he will propagate.

The process of improvement by selection will still be laborious but at least it will be possible.

Problem 5: Outcrossing.

The sheanut is an outcrosser, meaning that the trees are best pollinated by other shea trees that are of a different genetic makeup. Since the shea flowers must be pollinated before fruits and nuts can be produced a source of appropriate pollen must be nearby in the form of another, different but compatible shea tree. If another compatible tree has not come up at the proper distance from the first then the flowers will never be pollinated and no fruit will be produced.

This problem may be addressed by deliberately introducing compatible germplasm as a graft or a sapling providing that the parameters of successful pollination is properly investigated In some ways this is the least of the problems since many varieties of commercial fruit need pollination partners as well and there is much experience in setting up orchards to ensure pollination.

This dense cluster of intertwined horticultural problems make the shea tree much less useful than it should be and an extremely difficult species to work with.

A successful program of improvement, even at a rudimentary level could make the shea nut tree an important commercial crop. Information and improved seedlings distributed through the rural extension services could have a significant effect on the status income and well being of shea famers in six different African countries as well as preserving the long cycle/fallow tradition so necessary for preserving the topsoil in arid and semi arid areas.

If the shea tree is to reach its potential these obstacles to domestication be overcome and the farmer must gain some control over where the trees will grow. The farmer must also be guaranteed some reward for his labor and investment of time and inputs

Without change the shea crop cannot be made competitive and may disappear as the fallows cycle falls out of practice and land is used for vegetable and grain production.

As an example of hard to domesticate IFT the shea butter tree is perhaps a bit extreme.

But the horticultural problems of the shea butter tree are a prime example of linked and interdependent difficulties that must be overcome if this marvelous wild crop is to become a part of the continuum of human use.

Figure 2: Shea Tree

Chapter Sixteen
Marketing, Post Harvest and VAP

Marketing

Basic Use

There was only enough mealies for one meal a day at home. The rest of the time we ate fruit seeds and leaves from the trees in the bush.

This was said to me not by a honey hunter or herdsman but by a cabinet minister from Zimbabwe as he spoke of the hunger in his childhood.

Many IFT products are consumed on the spot by those who lack of food on their own table and are **supping at Gods table** instead.

This is the purest and most efficient use of the collected resource with no time or expense wasted on sorting, packing, advertising or shipping.

The products are usually at their maximum freshness and ripeness. The person who found, picked and ate the IFT product, derives at this time the most nutritional benefit.

The harvester may satisfy his hunger, then pick for family or home use.

The IFT product is then brought home and eaten fresh by others in the household, cooked as part of a meal or preserved for future use in the home.

IFT products may be shared with members of extended families or bartered with neighbors if there is a surplus.

Consequently much IFT produce never makes it to market, even to the most local village bazaar.

But even at that basic level if money or goods are exchanged for IFT products, a more demanding standard for the quality of the IFT product comes into play.

The village housewife will pick through the basket of black plums looking for fruit that is ripe but not bruised with skin undamaged.

The village shopper will choose only the perfect marula fruits if he or she is paying with cash or barter.

The seller in the local market will be able to move IFT in good condition. Damaged or overripe fruits may not be salable and will have to be made into a more stable product to be used.

Simple VAP

The most common VAP products made from IFT are dried foods, alcoholic beverages and preserves. These are all products that can be produced in the household to a high standard and are particularly suitable for the development of a small business or a cottage industry.

Dried IFT products: Wild fruits and other edible plant parts such as leaves, bark or flowers are often preserved by drying them in the sun and air. This is a simple process that requires little equipment and no infrastructure. Fruit, seeds, flowers, bark or leaves may be spread out in a thin layer to facilitate drying but the sun and the warm air do the rest Depending on the raw material and the season the drying process may take place in the full sunlight, in partial shade or full shade. The plant parts may be spread on cloths like figs or apricots, hung on racks for drying like tobacco leaves, bundled in a sheltered place like garlic bulbs or reduced to rings or strips like dried apples. Some fruits, like that of the Zisiphus, will dry on the tree. (See Figure 15 on page 226 and Figure 18 on page 227.)

The dried product will not easily rot or spoil and can be stored in any container that protects from moisture. Dried products are also considerably lighter than the products in their fresh state and so easier to transport.

It is true that drying certain fruits for market is not quite as simple as putting them out in the sun. Special driers are needed for particularly wet and fleshy fruits like mangoes if the resulting product is to be salable. Drying fruit is sometimes vulnerable to insects and birds. Fruits that become discolored in the drying process are often treated with sulfur or brushed with oil to make them retain a more attractive color.

Some areas are too damp for successful natural drying and drying has to be done in solar heated huts or in commercial ovens and driers.

While these methods of drying increase the expense of the operation they are more suitable for producing dried fruit for a more sophisticated market and may quickly pay for themselves.

For local use drying properly in the sun and air remains the cheapest method.

Simple drying frames that protect the product from full sunlight and insects can be made from local cloth and materials. The dried fruit can then be sold in paper or newspaper packets, avoiding packaging costs and keeping the price low.

Many of the most popular IFT products produced and sold locally in this manner are are leaf teas, spice, dried barks, dried whole fruits and fruit leathers. All of these are products that can be produced with a minimum of expense and inputs.

IFT derived alcohol: VAP products containing alcohol are considerably more complicated to produce. Large amounts of fermentable fruit or other material are required sometimes with the addition of sugar and yeast. Containers are needed for fermentation and later for sale of the product. The product must be strained, dated and labeled. Considerable infrastructure may be need for production and storage of the product. Purity and hygiene during production becomes an issue. Local and national governments, wary of amateur distilling operations but eager to tax cottage industries may have a considerable body of rules and regulations concerning the production use and sale of alcohol, IFT derived alcohol included.

But the proven profitability of the production of alcoholic beverages encourages IFT brewers and winemakers to overcome these problems. Brandies, beers and sweet liquors derived from IFT species are popular in local markets and slowly penetrating the global market, the most famous being Amarula, a sweet liquor made from marula fruit. (See Figure 26 on page 230.)

Jams jellies preserves and canned fruits: These forms of IFT based VAP require less infrastructure than alcohol production to produce but require the purchase of suitable containers to store and to sell the product and large quantities of sugar. The sugar, besides improving the flavor of the fruit is also the major preservative agent. The large amounts of sugar combined with the cooking process kills bacteria which causes mold or spoilage and making the product compact and storable. Jams and jellies made of IFT fruits are relatively common because of its relative ease in preparation and high trade value.

Canning fruits is more problematic than jam or jelly making because less sugar is added and the canning process must be done carefully to produce a safe product. Still successful vacuum canning can be done with a minimum of equipment as long as the basic rules of canning hygiene are followed and good quality inputs are purchased, especially jars and sealing rings.

(Canning in tins is already a professional operation needing machines, raw materials,, a bigger market and much expertise and cannot really be considered a small scale industry)

Sugar saturated fruits: Growing in popularity are the sugar saturated fruits and preparations like *cactus candy.*

These forms of VAP are made by forcing saturated sugar solution into strips or pieces of fruit and then drying them quickly in a heated chamber to form a hard surface.

Cactus fruits are often candied this way but other soft water filled fruits can be preserved in this manner including the papaya and the melon.

Salting food is one of the older methods of preparing it for sale, trade or storage. There are a few IFT species that when salted become as useful and edible as an olive. The caper, for instance may be salted or pickled in vinegar and oil. The same is true for the tamarind and the mango.

Because canning of vegetables is done at neutral ph, canning wild vegetables for sale is not always safe or easy. But packing in brine or vinegar is an excellent way to store vegetables and preserve them for use in the household or for sale.

Drying and salting is what preserves the mopane worm, considered a delicacy in most of Africa. This creature cannot be considered a true IFT product but the mopane worm is so associated with specific species of IFT that it must be mentioned. It is not the only insect associated with IFT species that is gathered for food. Also harvested and eaten are termites or white ants, grubs, mealworms, grasshoppers and bees which may be dried, eaten fresh, salted or fried in oil.

Insects Associated with IFT: In the Kasungu District of Malawi fourteen species of edible caterpillar are harvested regularly. Caterpillars feeding on the following IFT species are considered especially nutritious and tasty: Sclerocarya bierra, Burkea africana, and Colophosperum mopane.

Higher termite species are also a source of useful protein and are trapped as they fly from their nests in natural IFT stands on their dispersal flights. Processed they are eaten as relish or snacks. Snails raised on leaves gathered from IFT species or gathered in the wild also appear in the marketplaces of many African countries. They are usually sold while alive and consumed both live and cooked.

To quote the FAO Gender and Food Security website:

> *Insect species are high in vitamins and minerals. Caterpillars have been described as nature's vitamin pills. Bee larve contain ten times as much vitamin D as fish liver and twice as much vitamin A as egg yolk.*

Other Edible Products

Fungi: IFT species are often the host for mushrooms, bracket fungi and even truffles. In the markets of Kunming in the Yunnan province of China for instance twenty four edible species of fungus, gathered from the wild trees of the forests are among the most sought after local products. Seven species of edible mushroom are gathered in Uganda and 60 species of edible mushrooms that grow on leaf litter and dead wood are harvested in Malawi The prized truffles of Europe are growing on the roots of wild oaks. Chicken mushrooms, esteemed for their meaty flavor are found on logs of dead hardwood trees such as hickory and walnut. In the Pacific Northwest and British Columbia 25 to 50 million dollars is earned by mushroom pickers and fungi gatherers per year, making this kind of wild crafting one of the most profitable of the NWFP based endeavors.

Edible Leaves.

Leaves are one of the most widely consumed forest foods. They are used in soups, stews and side dishes. Some leaves are high in fat or protein. Young and tender leaves of IFT species such as Moringa oleides, Adansonia digitata and Afzelia quanzensis are rich in vitamins, essential minerals and oils. They are eaten fresh, boiled like spinach or cooked like relishes. Herbaceous plants associated with IFT species contribute significantly to the diet of rural households in Mozambique especially wild amaranths. In Swaziland wild leaves of Grewia species are eaten fresh during the spring and summer to supply vitamins or added to soups and stews.

Seeds

Seeds and nuts are high in calories protein and fats. Some very delicious and important trade foods are gathered from IFT species. Wild coconuts, wild oil palms and wild babassu palms are sources for hundreds of tons of wildcrafted oil per year. Seeds of IFT species such as the Narra melon can be dried and salted to make a nutritious and tasty snack while the kernel of the marula seed is the source of an excellent cooking oil. While most seeds and nuts need little processing, there are some, like the wild cashew that are poisonous before roasting and others that must be leached before they can be used safely. The local gatherers and consumers of the more problematic species should be consulted before the student or researcher attempts to deal with these seeds or nuts.

Honey, Wax, Bee Larve

Honey and beeswax are extremely important NWFPs associated with IFT species. Both are collected from wild hives in forest areas such as the miombo woodlands as well as from domesticated bees in agricultural land. Honey is an important food and sweetener, also used as raw material for alcoholic beverages and a curative substance in traditional medicine.

Beeswax has many applications including use in crafts, canning and finishing wooden furniture. Also important as a source of protein are the bee larve that are collected with honeycomb. They are generally eaten in the rural household though some are sold in village markets.

The bulk of honey and beeswax harvested and sold in Africa comes from rural households with a few hives though commercial beekeeping is becoming more popular. The source plants for most of the pollen and nectar needed by the bees are local herbaceous plants and IFT species. This gives African honey a richness and variability that has become an advantage in the marketplace.

Oil

Oil is the primary product of some IFT species like the shea butter and the argania spinosa and a secondary product of many other species such as the marula. The variability and usefulness of oil from IFT species is truly astounding. From medicinal oils like the oil of the Ti tree (Melaleucca alternifolia) to oils used in crafts like Tung oil or oils used in cosmetics and cooking, oil production from IFT species is looking more profitable and feasible than it ever has before.

Part of this new interest is due to improved extraction techniques and part of it is due to greater understanding of the value of unique oils, some of which have become expensive commodities.

Oil extraction can be accomplished with relatively primitive equipment. Argania oil, for instance, is made by Berber women who crush the kernals between grooved stones. Marula oil is produced in a similar manner. Animal driven grindstones are also a common and effective method of crushing oil seeds and nuts. Simple steam extraction with a few glass implements is a method to extract oil from leaves and flowers that needs little investment and infrastructure. (See Figure 28 on page 230 and Figure 29 on page 231.)

Saps

Sugary saps and gums are often fermented into wines and toddies, cooked into sweets or crystallized into sugary solids. These are high energy foods and very valued by indigenous population. Some of the aromatic saps are also edible but others have a high trade value and are used in making art material, for incense and perfume, medicine, food processing, electronics.

The most famous of the sugary saps is from the famous Maple tree and making maple syrup is a billion dollar industry in the northeastern US. (See Figure 27 on page 230.) Palm sugar from the Nipa palm is another well known sap product often sold in solid rounds in the Orient for cooking and sweetening. Lesser known IFT such as the Balanites aegypticus can also be tapped for a sugary sap. (See Figure 16 on page 226.)

VAP products which are not edible

Chew sticks and chew sponges. These plant parts are used primarily for cleaning teeth and promoting the health of mouth and gums. The neem tree is a source of chew sticks that are widely used in India instead of toothbrushes. Chewsponges sometimes have a similar function, though chewsponges are often harvested from plants with medicinal properties so chewing them delivers a low dose of a traditional medicine. There are also chew sticks and sponges used primarily because of a spicy or sweet taste.

Sponges

Some IFT species produce bark, pods or other materials esteemed for their usefulness when bathing. These sponges may be luffa like and fiberous or water absorbing pads, or used to work up a lather because of natural soap-like materials in the sponge.

Withies

Withies(flexible branches for crafts) raffia, and canes are harvested from a variety of IFT species, small fruits species and grasses. These extremely useful materials are very important to the rural economy being used to make baskets and craft items, furniture, building material, fencing material, roofing material, twine, trellis, fish and animal traps.

Bamboo

Bamboo is used primarily to make furniture, storage containers, cages and as building material for small rural buildings—though some types of bamboo produce edible shoots and others produce sections that are used to steam or cook food. Quick growing and easy to transplant bamboo is usually an underestimated and unreported resource of vital importance to the life of many rural households.

Fuel

Firewood and downed wood from wild trees and IFT species is a major source of energy in the impoverished countryside of the world. Often the women and girls of the third world must trek many kilometers a day or pay exorbitant prices for the wood to cook a meal for the family. The need for firewood is a major cause for deforestation and ecological destruction. Taking this into account it may be much easier to replant deforested areas with IFT species and other indigenous plants which produce a lot of downed wood then seeking to apply more high tech and expensive solutions. This way the firewood gatherers keep the forest free of flammable material and the locals enjoy a renewable energy source.

Smokewoods

Smokewoods are woods that are particularly fragrant when burned used as incense or to impart flavor to smoked food. Sandalwood, now an endangered species, is a good example of the wood that is used as incense. An excellent example from the United States of a flavoring tree is the mesquite tree used to fire traditional barbecues and in chile—making because of its rich underlying taste. Another example is the hickory tree that has been used traditionally in North America for smoking meat and fish.

Pestles and hardwood implements

Used in preparing staple foods the pestles and mortars must be made out of extremely durable wood. Not all IFT species are suitable, too many species, crack, warp, split or impart unpleasant tastes to the food. The shea butter tree is considered one of the best pestle making woods but there are many other suitable woods among IFT species.

Leaf wrappings

Leaves from wild trees or IFT species are used to wrap other foods, in a green state or dried into paper like materials. Leaves are sometimes used to contain food as it is steamed or cooked, something like the use of corn shucks to make tamales or sometimes in cooking pits as a protective layer between coal of fire and the food. Sometimes the leaves themselves are also edible.

Other materials include dye stuffs, shoots, leaves and flowers for plant arrangements, bark and roots for specialized purposes (such as briar roots for making pipes) inner bark for linings and basketry.

These materials have high trade value un—worked and sold to craft and hobby shops. But when presented as a finished product they can be a serious source of income for the IFT craftsman.

In the book Non Timber Forest Products, edited by Marla Emery and Rebecca J. McLain and published by Food Products Press (Haworth Press) in 2001 a table on page forty gives the prices of First People craft objects made of bark, fibers, wood, leather and feathers from British Columbia and sold by indigenous craftspeople.

The value of these items in US dollars is quite astonishing

Presenting the Product

IFT products must reach markets in a state of preparation and packaging that will make the consumer want to buy them and the merchant desire to stock them.

Crafted items that can be marketed to tourists are perhaps the easiest IFT products to market as they do not spoil and most can be shipped or stored without problem.

IFT food products are entirely another matter and must be made to exacting standards for a wider market

It is also important not to market an IFT food or medicine product prematurely. With new products the producer may only have once chance to impress the consumer. If the impression is negative and the product is stale, moldy, unripe, badly packed or spoiled it is unlikely that the consumer will ever be tempted to sample the product again.

Many IFT food products are superior nutritionally and in taste to products of cultivated plants.

If a fraction of the ingenuity, marketing skills and expertise lavished on conventional foods could be applied to IFT based products their place in the economy would be assured and many new foods and products would come out of the wilds areas to fill unfilled needs, delight the palate and educate the ecologically minded consumer as well as support IFT cultivation and provide income for the IFT gatherer or farmer.

Chapter Seventeen
IFT species in Windbreaks, Hedgerows, Margins

Many IFT species are well suited to the borders and margins of cultivated areas.

The IFT species may have a protective role to mitigate windspeed or heat and help create a microcimate. Or the species may be used as a living fence keeping domesticated animals in and wild animals out. Or an IFT planted area might be reservoir for insect eating birds, pollinating insects and bats and benfical organisms that help keep the cultivated lands healthy and in balance.

Whatever role the IFT plays in the hedgerows, windbreaks and margins the extreme hardiness and adaptability of the IFT species, their many variant forms and their resistance to challenging environments make them excellent margin plants. The fact that they produce usable and edible material as well often appears as an added bonus. In the margins the physical characteristics of the IFT species show their value as well as their possible products.

Windbreaks

Well designed windbreaks dramatically reduce wind speed and improve crop performance in wind stressed areas.

The microclimate of a field or farm can be mitigated or manipulated by planting trees especially for the purpose of breaking the force of the prevailing winds.

In areas where summers are hot trees and large shrubs have a cooling effect on their lee sides when a breeze blows through them. Screens of vegetation protect an area from dust and pollutants by filtration. Since wind speed is slowed by vegetation suspended particles tend to drop out leaving the air on the other side of the planting both cleaner and reduced in force and temperature.

In cold areas the lee side of a wind breaking line will be warmer and less vulnerable to the freeze—drying effect of a cold north wind.

Diverting the wind by using living windscreens is useful art for the farmer and gardener. A conventional wood frame building will be as much as 10 percent warmer or cooler if protected from the wind. Windscreens slow erosion in plowed fields and decrease the rate of evaporation in protected gardens. Areas that need to be shielded should be evaluated carefully and species of wind screening trees should be chosen that are vigorous but not invasive, fast growing but have other useful attributes besides their height.

The shape and density of the windscreen planting may have profound influence on the protected area.

Dense plantings that stop the wind like a wall are locally effective but may cause damaging downward turbulence or create a funnel like area where all the force of the wind on the wind breaking line rushes through a gap or presses against a corner.

Vegetation that is planted less thickly but with more depth is often a more efficient windbreak than a single closely planted line. In a planting with more depth the wind is not stopped but its force is very much reduced over a distance of several tree lengths and some air gets through. It is important that air continue to flow as fields and gardens with poor air circulation may be susceptible to frost in cool areas or swelter in unrelieved heat and dust in warmer areas.

As the height of a windbreak increases so does the protected area to the lee side of the planting. How much area is protected and the quality of that protection depends very much on the planting depth and density and the species chosen for planting.

The native IFT species should be the first candidates for windscreen plantings and groves as they are already adapted to local conditions and can be planted around a field or dwelling with little fear of ecological disruption to the area.

As a general rule the hardier and more useful IFT species should be chosen but one factor that cannot be ignored when IFT species are used to protect fields or gardens is the relative aggressiveness of the root system.

IFT species that gather moisture from exceptionally large areas tend to have very invasive root systems. These trees may compete with the plants they are supposed to be protecting and in extreme cases will choke the other plants out.

Thorny or spiny trees that regenerate quickly are often favored as windbreaks as they can double as fences that keep stock out and provide a certain amount of forage and browse to the animals as well.

Another factor that should be taken into account is the primary product of the IFT species. Species that produce a primary product attractive to larger creatures among the local wildlife may be problematic as windbreaks for gardens and farms.

A fourth factor in IFT choice for windscreen plantings is the strengths and vulnerabilities of the tree itself. Obviously trees vulnerable to frost should not be deployed to stop chilly north winds and understory trees, used to being shaded by the giants of the upper canopy should not be planted to stop the scorching winds from the south.

Frost tolerant and cold tolerant conifers and hardy wind cutting trees like poplars and cottonwoods are available to stop chilling winds in temperate zones.

In warmer areas the cypress the eucalyptus and the deodar are often found on the north side of a protected area.

On the southern sides of protected areas that are exposed to the hot sand laden winds from desert, trees such as the tamarisk, the causarina, the acacia and the lalob are often planted

Even in sparse ecosystems there is enough diversity among local IFT species to find the appropriate windscreen trees and they should be the preferred species for windbreak planting whenever possible.

IFT in hedgerows

Hedgerows is an old English term that refers to narrow planted strips along fields, fence lines, roads, and waterways.

Hedgerows are planted to serve many purposes and perform many functions. They may serve as wildlife corridors or sources of nectar and pollen for bees. They may be a refuge for edge species that thrive where two habitats come together.

Hedges may serve as barrier to stock, keeping animals out of the vegetable gardens or fields of grain or keeping them in as a living fence for field sized corrals.

Trees, shrubs and herbaceous plants used as hedges can add to farm income by producing useful material. Hedges may be a source of firewood, lumber, medicinal herbs, cuttings and seeds, small fruit or leaves for tea, fungi, nuts, roots and shoots.

Coppiced hedgerows can supply withies or craft material. Tool handles and garden implements are sometimes crafted from the uncommon woods of hedgerow plants.

Hedgerows protect livestock from extreme temperatures.

Some hedges are planted to supplement stock grazing. In the dry areas of Mexico, pigs, goats and cattle may eat the leaves and fruit of the prickly pears that surround their pasture. In temperate climate alder hedges provide a supplementary food rich in nitrogen, hazel hedges will be grazed by milk cows, willow and gorse browsed by sheep. While the main trunks of the hedge planted may need to be protected by tree guards the nibbling and browsing of animals most often has a strengthening effect.

Hedges may mark boundaries, stop the noise from busy roads and slow down potentially damaging air currents. Strong winds can cause grain and grass crops to lodge making harvest difficult. Plants subjected to wind stress put down deeper roots and have less energy for growth causing smaller and later yields.

Hedgerows provide a barrier to trap soil particles and slow water flow making cultivated areas less vulnerable to erosion. They also conserve water by reducing evaporation and storing run—off from plowed fields. The hedgerows are a source of green manures, leaf mould and mulches. They tend to mitigate the temperature of soil and air. Hedgerows filter dust from the air and supply safe living space for songbirds, pollinators, predators and beneficial insects.

In the north of England it is still possible to see hedgerows in the agricultural landscapes. These traditional protective barriers of plants and plant stems, pruned severely and then woven together are unique features of the northern landscape and have a profound influence on the areas they define. (See Figure 31 on page 232.)

They separate fields of wheat from meadows where sheep and cattle graze, line footpaths, run along the banks of steams and canals. They are often composed of thorny untidy plants such as brambles or minor fruits such as currant bushes or closely planted trees such as yew. (See Figure 30 on page 231.)

The fields and the grazing areas look much as wheat fields and pastures do everywhere else but the hedgerows are dense and teem with life.

Songbirds nest and feed in the hedgerows, foxes, hedgehogs and pheasants scurry along them and shelter under them, kestrels hover over them seeking prey.

The hedgerows break the cold north wind and flocks will huddle on the sheltered side of a hedge to stay warm. Snow piles up in winter and melts into the ground making hedgerows reservoirs of soil moisture. Undisturbed by the plow hedgerows are the refuge and breeding ground for earthworms and dozens of other beneficial creatures of the soil.

The role of the hedgerow in stopping erosion is only beginning to be understood. Thousands of miles of hedgerows were destroyed in the south of England in a misguided drive to modernize agriculture. The result was an 800% rise in the amount of soil lost to wind and water erosion.

The role of the hedgerow in the regeneration of soil populations is only beginning to be noticed as well. Since hedgerows are not plowed they become reservoirs and shelters for vast populations of soil organisms killed or harmed by plowing and the application of fertilizer. These organisms recolonize the soil of the fields from the hedgerow after soil trauma and do much to restore balance in cultivated fields.

With no hedgerow to shield these tiny creatures and fields plowed to the shoulders of roads there is no sheltered population of soil life to aid in rebalancing and regenerating the soil. The healing process in hedgerow—less fields takes much longer and sometimes never happens at all.

Soils in fields without protected margins lose their tilth quality at a faster rate, are more prone to wind and water erosion, generally contain less nitrogen and potassium and do not as readily hold water.

Some IFT species in very settled areas have survived primarily as hedgerow plants. Other IFT species are very suitable for inclusion in hedges because of their multiple products and their physical characteristics or for use as living fences.

Living fences can be considered a very specialized sort of hedge. The plants are primarily chosen for their physical toughness, hardiness, resistance to damage by animals and value as browse to the animals.

Suitable plants are available for almost all ecological conditions.

Of course living fences can have all the advantages of hedgerows in providing feed, food, fibers, shade, windbreak, material for medicines and refuge to wildlife predators and pollinators.

Like other hedges they need care to be effective, they must be pruned and staked,, sometimes woven and suckered. If untended they can compete with field crops for water and fertilizer and if not pruned they can become overgrown.

Improved Fallows

More useful than a mere windbreak are the leguminous trees used for improved fallows.

These trees are almost always NFT species (Nitrogen Fixing Trees) and have the ability to take nitrogen from the air and pass it on other plants through the cycling of organic materials. Nitrogen is essential for healthy plant growth and NFT are a major source of nitrogen in tropical ecosystems. Planted in a garden or orchard format or integrated with conventional farming or agroforestry NFT species are excellent and inexpensive sources of soil nitrogen and leaf litter for mulch, greatly reducing the amount of fertilizer that must be purchased.

Planted between fields of vegetables and maize in poor African countries like Malawi the trees improve the soil as they grow. Aside from their contribution s of nutrients and organic matter NFTs have many uses on the farm including fodder, leaf protein, salad material, apiary plants, wind shelter and living fences. NFT are often found in shambas, providing support and shelter for more vulnerable plants. (See Figure 32 on page 232.)

Some continue to grow until the vegetable plot becomes a grove, others are felled and burned so that the ash may also enrich the soil. Improved fallows trees sometimes double as shade producers and windbreaks, becoming a regular features in the garden and allowing lesser plants to benefit from their dropped leaves, their nitrogen fixing ability and their physical protection.

Other margins

The **woodlot**, the protected watershed, the house orchard and the market grove are four among many marginal areas that can be benefited by the presence of IFT species. In many of these settings IFT are already filling a role.

Woodlots are areas of semi domesticated trees that are usually kept for sap, fruit, nuts timber and firewood. Woodlots often resemble miniature managed forests and the IFT species are generally forest trees such as walnuts, hickories, beeches, maples and conifers The use of woodlots and woodlot products has begun to rise after nearly 50 years of decline in the US, England and Canada probably due to the rise in the price of oil and gasoline. (See Figure 17 on page 227.)

Protected water sheds are also usually planted in forest trees, temperate or tropical with an emphasis on those with strong root systems. These trees have been planted or left in a large area above and upstream from a tributary and their purpose is to slow the rate of water flow and absorb as much water and soil as possible to keep riparian areas from being damaged and streams from overflowing. Timbering off protected watersheds is often disastrous for all life downstream as rain water overwhelms the streambed and washes earth, houses, roads, trees and bushes away. This type of misuse of forest resources is the primary cause of landslides in areas with heavy rainfall

House orchards are usually planted with fruit trees or trees that produce sap nuts or other materials for the farmstead while also contributing shade, wind screening and some firewood to the home. The wild relatives of domesticated trees such as the crab apple and truly wild trees already a few steps up the path of domestication can often be found together in this format. The Middle Eastern and Mediterranean version of the house orchard, the **bustan**, is usually planted in hardy citrus such as lemons with date palms and olive trees contributing fruit, shade and oil to the household.

The market grove is part of the village commons and can be seen in many small communities worldwide. Large trees have been planted or simply left unmolested through the years to make a shady square or town center for holding open air markets, town meetings, operate favorite cafes or simply providing a place for the citizen to sit at leisure and watch the life of the community. While market square trees are almost always surrounded by shops and private dwellings, they provide homes for a surprising amount of wildlife, birds and beneficial insects, especially those which become easily used to the presence of human beings.

IFT species roles and possibilities are numerous for marginal areas and can be used to replace aging trees and plants or planted to create new stands of fast growing protective plants.

The distinct characteristics and properties of IFT species are more clearly seen on the margins simply because their vigor, and value are not appreciated in more abundant and sheltered format.

This will change as more IFT species come with the continuum of human use especially in marginal areas and marginal lands.

Chapter Eighteen
The IFT Species and the New Agrarianism

From an ecological point of view modern agriculture has had truly disastrous effects on soil, water resources and agricultural communities.

One does not have to look far anywhere in the world to find eroded soil, polluted water and shrinking and dying farm communities—all of them killed paradoxically by the very activity that once sustained them.

The advantages of factory farming are all on the side of the businessman, the middleman and the retailer. To the people who actually grow the food, the farms and the farmed organisms the modern system has been cruel and destructive at best.

At its worst the modern agricultural system puts the farmer out of business, the land out of production and causes the farming community, its economic wellsprings dried up, to wither away as countless other towns and villages across the world have already done.

The cultivation and development of IFT must not follow the same path towards destruction.

The formal inclusion of IFT species in the agricultural continuum must be done in a manner that serves the rural people who depend on the trees for food and income. It must be done in a way that will regenerate rather than degrade the land.

And it must be done in a way that still allows the hungry, the landless, the women and the children of the rural areas, far from the seats of power and the places where research is done, to participate and benefit from this immense, ignored and untapped resource.

We must therefore avoid as many of the mistakes of the conventional agricultural ethic as is humanly possible during the process of including IFT.

IFT species should first be cultivated as local crops to feed and support local people for they are the people too often overlooked by the powers that be.

IFT must not be removed from the global commons and become the property of one company or another. There are already too many obstacles to making a living in the rural areas of the world. Patenting IFT species would probably not facilitate domestication and development but it would deprive thousands of rural poor of a critical source of food and income.

IFT species are already hardy, already disease resistant already in tune with their area and locales. Perhaps it is not necessary to change them to include them into agricultural systems.

Perhaps it makes more sense to change the systems themselves.

The Need for Durable Systems of Agriculture

IFT species are unique resources, their hardiness, adaptability, disease resistance and ability to flourish in low energy sustainable formats a welcome contrast to the overbred and pampered, chemical soaked conventional crops of the day.

These species can be a vital element in the rise of new community centered rather than production centered forms of agriculture. To quote from the introduction of *The New Agrarianism:Land Culture and the Community of Life:*

> *With no fanfare and indeed hardly much public notice agrarianism is again on the rise. In small corners and pockets in ways for the most part unobtrusive people are reinvigorating their ties to the land, both in their practical modes of living and in the ways they think about themselves, their communities and the good life. Agrarianism, broadly conceived reaches beyond food production and rural living to include a wide constellation of ideas, loyalties, sentiments and hopes. It is a temperament and a moral orientation as well as a suite of economic practices all arising out of the insistent truth that people everywhere are a part of the land community, just as dependent on the lands fertility and just as shaped by its mysteries and possibilities Agrarian comes from the Latin word* **agrarius** *pertaining to the land and it is the land as place, home and living that anchors the agrarian scale of values.*

Eric Freyfogle

The agrarianism of the 21st century, often high tech and academic, usually ecologically motivated may seem to be very far from the concerns and practices of wild rubber tappers and subsistence farmers in the developing world.

But the distance between intentions and practices of the old agrarianism and the new is not as great as is commonly perceived.

An agrarian is not a person wishing to return to an idealized past but a person determined to safeguard the future of the land, the living elements of the agricultural system and the communities and cultures of people who make their living from the land.

An agrarian is a person who sees in the countryside the possibilities of abundance, conservation and kindly use instead of the weird modern duality of a totally artificial monocultural and sterile agriculture and a totally unspoiled nature—with either side of the coin making no provisions for people who actually live in rural areas.

Agrarians do not wish to abandon the countryside to the developer and the corporate farm or the task of preserving the thousands of varieties of cultivated plants to those who do not see their importance.

Both the old and new agrarians are attempting to protect, nurture and preserve the fertility and carrying capacity of the land. Both groups use diverse sets of tools and skills to make a living and practice good stewardship in relation to local creatures, communities, water and soil. Both groups are dedicated to the ethics and practical application of a durable agriculture, one that is economically and culturally stable, one that can be practiced to support those alive today without impoverishing and cheating those who will live from the land tomorrow.

To quote Wendell Berry's paper The Whole House from the previously mentioned book:

> *An agrarian economy is always a subsistence economy before it is a market economy. The center of an agrarian farm is the household. The function of the household economy is to assure that the farm family lives so far as possible from the farm. It is the subsistence part of the agrarian economy that assures its stability and its survival. A subsistence economy necessarily is highly diversified and it characteristically has involved hunting and gathering as well as farming and gardening. These activities bind people to their local landscape by close, complex interests and economic ties. The industrial economy alienates people from the native landscape precisely by breaking these direct practical ties and introducing distant dependencies. Agrarian people of the present knowing the land must be well cared for if anything is to last, understand the need for a settled connection not just between farmers and their farms but also between urban people and their surrounding and tributary landscapes. Because the knowl-*

> *edge and know how of good care—taking must be handed down to children, agrarians recognize the necessity of preserving the coherence of families and communities.*

Conventional agriculture unfortunately is often practiced as if there will be no tomorrow with scant regard for any living institution or thing—especially families and communities. Rather than being lamented the disappearance of the family farm and the farming town often has been celebrated as a sign of progress.

This kind of agriculture cannot be sustainable or durable as it ignores the well being of the living elements of agricultural production. Since measures that protect the soil, the water, the farm community or the farmed plants and animals by their very nature must reduce the margin of profit, these measures are simply not taken.

The profit margin of such system may be great and continue to rise for a time but conventional agriculture systems inflate immediate productivity at the expense of future productivity in the same way that spendthrift consumers overspend their credit.

This system is also based on the notion that there will always be other farms to take over and consolidate, other wilderness areas to develop, ignoring the finite nature of soil and water resources.

Also ignored is the finite nature of the one resource that turns the tractor wheels, transports the factory—farmed goods and produces cheap chemical fertilizer for the fields.

Oil is most assuredly a finite resource, one that is increasing in price day by day and one that cannot last forever

It is likely that conventional agriculture, neither flexible, nor conserving nor diverse and exceedingly dependent on cheap energy, will not survive the era of cheap oil.

IFT Species in Durable Agricultural Systems

The true raison d etre for agriculture is the production of good food to sustain the farmers and farm communities and to nourish with the surplus those who do not farm but are able to pay in money or bartered goods for the food they need but do not produce.

The farmer then receives cash to buy what the farm cannot produce or commodities that are not locally available.

Systems of this sort tend to be relatively simple and self regulating as regards to trade but diverse and complex regarding cultivation.

The tendency is towards livelihood farms and mixed operations with diverse crops and stock, year round production and employment and a regenerative attitude toward community and land.

IFT species fit very well into this sort of agriculture, their yields may be low(or inconveniently copious) but so is the input from the farmer. The products of the IFT species may be diverse, but so are the needs of the farmstead. IFT may be wild but wildness in the hedgerow and the woodlot is beneficial for the small farm as pollinators and predators, all of them needed to sustain the balance of the crop systems, may shelter or be sustained by the bounty of the IFT species.

As IFT species are domesticated and brought more surely into the continuum of use controversy will surely arise as to whether the IFT species should be changed to fit into the strait jacket of modern agriculture or be utilized and improved as an element in the new or old agrarian farmstead.

But with so vast an unused resource it is surely possible to use IFT in all stages of agricultural development and for reasons and purposes as diverse as the IFT species themselves.

As IFT species enter agricultural systems from subsistence farming to agroforestry to plantation formats their unique qualities should be treasured and preserved. That an IFT tree such as the marula is able to thrive without much water or fertilizer in an orchard format is a testimony to the trees hardiness, not a sign that the marula produces an inferior fruit.

IFT trees growing in extreme or marginal areas are able to do so because of their strength and adaptability—not because they are useless weeds that produce nothing of value.

IFT species are able to grow and produce food and many other products in areas too challenging for conventional cultivars.

They are able to survive in depleted land and to aid in the restoration of damaged land. They are in themselves a regenerative phase of land recovery as any farmer knows who has seen eroded gullied land colonized by seedlings and saplings and turned back to forest again.

In the domestication and utilization of IFT species the new agrarians and the traditional agrarians can find common ground and easily cooperate.

For the agrarian of any style the IFT species can be the small fruits of the hedgerow and the thorns of living fence. They can produce fruit in the house orchard or be trimmed into firewood in the woodlot.

They can shade the house from the sun, break the wind that sweeps across the garden, support the hammock in the back yard.

They can provide browse and pods for the goats and sheep and seeds and flowers to feed the poultry.

Quoting Mr. Berry again: *An agrarian economy rises up from the fields woods and—streams, from the complex of soils, slopes, weathers and connections influences and exchanges that we mean when we speak, for example of the local community or the local watershed. The agrarian mind is therefore not regional or national, let alone global but local. It must know on intimate terms the local plants and animals and local soils, it must know the local possibilities and impossibilities, opportunities and hazards. It depends and insists on knowing very particular local histories and biographies.*

IFT species belong in the landscape. They are a part of the vast web of connections, influences and exchanges between insect, animal and bird, between plan and plant and between the land and the people who live on the land.

The lore of IFT must concern the mind of the agrarian, both new and traditional. This body of knowledge is entwined in the opportunities and hazards and the histories and narratives of each locale.

For those attempting to forge a durable and sustainable way of living from the land, while taking care of the land, the IFT species are an immensely valuable treasure chest of possibilities and resources waiting to be integrated.

Welcoming kindly use.

Chapter Nineteen
Orchards for Extreme Environments?

IFT species have qualities that make them survivors in extreme conditions. They are often very hardy as to temperature, altitude and weather events. Some IFT species can deal with low or high ph or excess iron or other minerals in the soil. This makes them regenerative and reclamative plants of great value but it also points to the possibilities inherent in using IFT research to find crops for extreme areas of all types.

With much arable land in decline or depleted and urbanization gobbling up yesterdays farmland—agriculture is being forced into more and more marginal areas.

IFT species are already adapted to marginal areas, challenging conditions and stressful environments.

It is in these challenging conditions that IFT species reveal their great strengths and adaptability.

Desert Agriculture.

Agriculture has flourished in deserts because of human skill in diverting water and irrigating arid lands. But desert soils are poor and fragile and the irrigation water that brings life to the desert also brings minerals and mineral salts that lead to the areas eventual salinization and decline.

The history of the Fertile Crescent is a cautionary tale for modern day advocates of irrigation, After thousands of years that once rich area is still in many places too saline to grow anything but barley and wild grass.

Most desert agriculture is not sustainable. The crops chosen for their market value alone are often water intensive crops like winter vegetables, or crops pushed into the desert from other areas and climates by urbanization of more appropriate farmland.

If desert agriculture is to continue steps must be taken to bring current practices closer to sustainability.

Salinization can be delayed by careful application of water and by cultivating plants suitable for arid and saline areas, plants which use little water and do not have to be continually irrigated to survive. Chemical soil amendments can be replaced by deep composting, pesticides and herbicides by IPM and appropriate mulching techniques. Changes in these practices would do much to make desert agriculture more ecologically friendly.

Still the challenges of the desert are formidable: High temperatures and wide temperature differentials kill all but the hardiest plants. Low relative humidity and swift evaporation of water make ground covers and mulches necessary for the effective use of water resources. Artificial shade, windbreaks and other protective measures allow crops to grow to maturity despite sandstorms and other weather events. It must be remembered however that desert agriculture is a precarious endeavor. In the desert badly designed agricultural projects can disappear overnight.

Luckily a goodly number of useful IFT species fit the profile of crop candidates for arid and saline areas including such powerful sources of useable material as the marula, the argania and the balanities.

Many of the trees esteemed in ancient times for their fragrances and medicinal properties may also be cultivated in a sustainable manner in arid and salty areas, as can some gum producing and many fodder producing trees.

These possible crop candidates should be investigated by the farmer or researcher as it is very important for the long term viability of the plantings that trees planted in the desert be physiologically appropriate.

High Altitude Agriculture

High altitudes zones closer to the equator seem similar to temperate zones in both the climate and the type of plants which do well there. But there are some serious differences due to unique factors that affect the growth and development of plant species.

High altitude zones close to the equator are warmer than high altitude zones of greater latitude because the sun rays strike a smaller area The sunlight is intense at high altitudes and the air is thin so the atmosphere absorbs less of the shorter wavelength of light(such as UV). The sun angle is higher than in temperate zones resulting in less shade, high soil surface temperatures and more evaporation from the soil surface.

Hedges and windbreaks are needed in high altitude orchards to slow evaporation and protect from the drying effect of the winds. Hedges and windbreaks are also good protection for high altitude soils against extreme weathering and erosion from wind and water. Soil protection and conservation techniques of all kinds are necessary to preserve the fertility and topsoil of high altitude slopes.

Short days result in less photosynthetic activity and together with low average temperature may cause crops to require more time to mature at high altitudes. Plants for high altitudes should be selected for their adaptation to specific daylengths. While it is known that some IFT species are day length neutral, the day length requirements of most wild trees have never even been researched.

Deep composting beds that generate heat have proved effective in the nurture of plants at altitudes approaching 3000 meters. The warm fertile beds full of material that continues to decompose and so raise ground temperature have been successful in preventing frost damage in most cultivated plants and especially helpful in giving perennial plants a good start.

Growing plants in greenhouse under glass or plastic has also proved possible at these altitudes—though this is not practical plan for most orchards.

Another high altitude trial for introduced plants is the extremes of temperature common in highlands. A span of 40 degrees Celsius is possible in the same day in some places insuring that only the most temperature hardy plants will survive in that locale

Microclimates and climatic instability characterize many mountainous areas as the complex mosaic of mountains and valleys lead to marked differences in temperature within small areas. Mountainous topography also produces wide variations in soil type and fertility.

Nowhere is agriculture more local than in these areas. Rain, hail, frost, drying winds and pest cycles are more difficult to predict with variations extreme enough to cause real problems in agriculture. Traditional farmers in the Andean highlands cope with the resulting instability and uncertainty by maintaining diverse crops, staggering plantings and working plots at different altitudes.

Sustainable IFT planting in high altitude low latitude zones will probably require similar local knowledge and similar diversification strategies to be successful.

High altitude zones in temperate areas also present special challenges. One of the most severe is a climate produced by the interplay between a short growing season, thin air and low temperatures. This does not mean there is not set of IFT food plants that fit into to high altitude temperate zones. Indeed, there are many minor fruits, nuts, fungi, and herbs that thrive in higher altitudes of temperate zones and very few of these plants have been domesticated or even investigated.

J. Russel Smith, author of Tree Crops, dreamed of founding a school for mountain agriculture and producing food, fodder and non timber forest products. While this dream did not become a reality several serious organizations have begun to evaluate and try to improve the food producing capabilities of mountainous areas.

To mention a few of these organizations, there is the Sustainable Mountain Agricultural Center of Kentucky, the Integrated Center for Mountain Development of India, The Sustainable Mountain Agriculture Program for the Hindu Kush range, The Lesotho Mountain Center for Investment in Agriculture, The Shaanxi Development Program for Mountain Agricultural in the Quinling Mountains, the Sustainable Mountain Gardening Forums of the USA, the Men Tsee Khang Center for Tibetan Plants in Dharamsala.

No cookie cutter short cut to agriculture is applicable to these challenging areas. Yet these areas are populated by people who support themselves, their families and their animals in what looks to most of us like sparse and forbidding environments.

There are many ways sound methods of R and D may help the mountain agriculturalists to develop wild mountain plant resources. And there is much the modern agricultural researcher can learn in these zones about sustainable cultivation, appropriate technology, patience and thrift.

Acid Soil

In the humid tropics acidification of the soil is a natural process and one that greatly affects plant growth. As soils become more acid and the ph drops down to 4. 5 or lower it becomes very difficult to produce food crops. Some minerals such as aluminum become more soluble and more toxic. Many plant nutrients become more limited in supply. This is especially so in weathered areas.

The main reasons for soil acidity is the production of carbon dioxide by the plants in quantities that sometimes causes the amount of $CO2$ in the soil to be many times that of CO^2 in the air.

Many forms of organic matter can be acidifying depending on the plant from which the matter is derived. Many plants contain organic acids. As their residues decompose the organic acids exert influence on the soil acidity.

Other plants have low percentages, of basic compounds. If the plant does not contain enough compounds to support the microbial life necessary for the decomposition of plant debris much carbon dioxide is produced and base nutrients such as calcium and magnesium are removed from the soil in the process.

Plant growth contributes to acidification since a major nutrient uptake is to exchange hydrogen ions on the root surfaces and take up needed base ions such as calcium, potassium and magnesium.

Other contributing factors to soil acidity are: acid rain, the tendency of acid soils to fix phosphate, base ion displacement and leaching and the release of potentially toxic substances like aluminum at pH under 5.5.

As a general rule tropical soils tend to be acid as well as soils of drained swamp and wetlands and the soil of rainforests. All these soil types tend to be low in fertility.

A major cause of acidification in cultivated soil is the nature and amount of chemical fertilizers used. These chemicals can become a major source of hydrogen ions. Ammonium is usually given as the nitrogenous component in PKN applications and the oxidation of ammonium to nitrates is accompanied by the release of hydrogen ions.

Ph adjustment has been a goal in acid soils since agriculture began though the farmers of those times did not understand precisely why applying crushed shells, or wood ash improved soil fertility (It was not until the 1800s that a Virginia farmer deduced that such a practice decreased soil acidity).

Practices such as the addition of finely crushed oyster shells, coral sands and crushed limestone have been used to mitigate soil acidity for thousands of years.

The oldest de acidification strategy however is the deliberate clearing by fire of vegetated areas The most obvious source of nutrients in tropical areas is found in the above ground vegetation. Nutrients are released by burning the current vegetation for the cultivation of food crops grown in the ash. Base ions such as potassium, calcium and magnesium will cause the ash to be alkaline thus reducing some of the acidity.

In traditional sustainable farming systems the fire—cleared area is planted with a combination of annuals, biennials and perennials and cropped for a few years before the surrounding location vegetation recovers. This is a sustainable practice providing the average fallow time is sufficient for recovery of the vegetation, usually no less than twenty years. If an area is burned and cropped at frequent intervals the soil loses structure, fertility declines and the returning vegetation will not be able to restore the area.

IFT orchards planted sustainably in acid soils will most like resemble the shamba or at least be an integrated planting of companion species such as coffee, naranjilla and Inga verra (ice cream bean).

The reason for this is the precarious nature of tropical soils themselves, easily depleted, easily lost to water erosion, easily lost to the return of native vegetation.

Saline soil

Salt occurs naturally in soils from rocks and minerals and is present in all water except rainwater. When water evaporates or wicks away, these salts are left behind. Chemical fertilizers given in the form of chemical salts contribute to soil salinity as does the irrigation of cropland with mineralized water. Floodwaters in arid and saline areas may bring salts dissolved in the run off water into previously salt free areas. For many reason soil salinity tends to build up over the years, making cultivated areas less productive and sometimes making agriculture impossible.

Salt in the soil makes water less available to plants because salt ions attract water. Flocculation of soil particles, especially clay cause blockage of soil pores, making it much hard for water to infiltrate and causing the crusting seen on the surface of saline soil.

Many saline soils are waterlogged soils, a result of unwise irrigation practices or of a naturally high water table. This is a poor situation for plant growth as plants in waterlogged soil cannot take in sufficient oxygen and because of this tend to be weak and yellowed.

Many plants have the capability to excrete a certain amount of salt taken in by their roots but they cannot do this when standing in water.

Many desert soils are saline soils as explained in the beginning of the chapter but saline soils are also found on coasts, in mountainous regions and in areas where arable land has been ruined by unwise farming and irrigation.

Saline soils are characterized by their electrical conductivity. The unit of measure is the sieman and the Electrical Conductivity of soils is measured in decisiemans per square meter.

The salinity of water is measured in a similar way. Good quality irrigation water will have from 0 to 1 decisieman per meter, marginal or poor water from 1-3 per meter, saline groundwater from 4—7. Water from the Pacific ocean measure 46 decisieman per meter. If these measurements are expressed in parts per million, fresh water contain only 100 to 120 parts per million salt, slightly saline water from 125 to 250 parts per million salt, moderately saline water contains 250 to 500 parts per million salt and saline water from 500 to 2,500 parts per million salt.

Saline soils can be made less saline by good agricultural practices such as restoring drainage, adding organic material to improve the soil tilth and friability and leaching the soil with fresh water. Organic material also improves water infiltration rates, and acidifies the soil making calcium compounds available and easier to leach out, an important process since excess and insoluble calcium are the main byproducts of salinization.

Very saline soils can be treated with gypsum, a source of soluble calcium, to allow for more efficient leaching. Adding acids to the soil has the same effect, the acids make the calcium soluble and therefore leachable. While expensive on a large scale these methods are effective in groves and gardens that have been contaminated by saline floodwater or seawater.

IFT planting in saline environments will be successful if salinity is managed and the chosen species are salt tolerant.

Regular irrigation with drip lines keeps salinity low around the root ball. A good program of composting and mulching provides nutrients for the plants, improves the permeability of the soil and decreases evaporation.

Growing salt tolerant plants will improve the soil and the environment over time. Among the cultivated plants there are a few which tolerate brackish and saline water with little ill effect such as the beet and the date palm. Many other palms are salt tolerant such as the Nipa palm. Among the fruit trees the zisiphus varieties are quite salt tolerant as are the sapodillas (Manikara sp). Balanites, guava and rose apples seem to have considerable salt tolerance as do many of the leguminous trees grown for fodder such as the tamarugo and mesquite.

IFT Possibilities for Extreme Orcharding

In short IFT species have great promise in challenging areas for what can best be termed extreme orcharding.

The farmer and researcher at this point must use his own judgment and intelligence while searching for IFT species that might be fit for these areas.

Obviously IFT species from arid and saline areas will have the best change of successful development in similar areas. This is true as well for locales that have other specialized conditions.

The physiological suitability of the species will also be an important factor as well as basic water needs and tolerances.

But considering the wide array of IFT types and species and their great strength and adaptability the serious investigation of IFT species will surely lead to the discovery of crop candidates for extreme environments.

Chapter Twenty
Books and Resources

Books

For a researcher a good book on a subject dear to the heart is like a trustworthy companion on a very long journey.

Besides the useful information, the confirmation of facts and figures and the shared sympathies and intent there is the inevitable feeling of gratitude to the author.

I have often felt that I can do my work only because of those who came and observed, worked and wrote before me. Sometimes the gap between my work and theirs is one of decades, sometimes only a few years but the feeling that these writers and scientists (some of them long dead) are walking along the path beside me is very reassuring.

I hope some day that some young scientist or researcher will feel that way about my book.

Meanwhile here is a list of the books that have helped me very much on every level of the writing process from supplying needed facts and figures to fueling my desire to design and describe a less destructive kind of agriculture.

Some of these books are out of print but well worth reading.

Tree Crops, A Permanent Agriculture, J. Russel Smith, Harper Colophon Books, 1950. This important study of the potential of tree crops to change the dynamics of agriculture is a must for anyone interested in arboriculture, IFT or perennial crops. The book is currently out of print but can be obtained through the book search sites of Amazon and Barnes and Noble.

Tree Medicine, Peter Conway, Piatkus Publishing, 2001. A handy, very readable encyclopedia of medicinal trees, illustrated, listing many plants close to extinction.

Deciduous Orchards, W. H. Chandler, Henry Klimpton, London, 1957. Basic orchard information about the most common of deciduous tree crops, including pruning, and post harvest treatment of fruit written in the 1950s, a classic horticultural tome.

Evergreen Orchards, WH. Chandler, Lea and Febiger Publications, Philadelphia 1958. another classic by the same author, W. H. Chandler who was Professor of Horticulture at the University of California 1930-50.

Fruits For Warm Climates, Julia F. Morton published by the author, 1987. An astounding encyclopedia of scores of little known, unknown and wild fruit crops with many photographs and much information about origin and cultivation.

The Concise Encyclopedia of Temperate Tree Crops edited by Baugher and Singha, Viva Books 2005—a series of articles and papers covering most aspects of temperate arboriculture, from some very common sense descriptions of grafting experiments to more challenging works.

Return to Resistance, Raoul Robinson, agAcess, Davis California, 1996. An elegant masterpiece explaining the theory of field resistance, marking the path for those who want to get out of the pesticide spiral and expounding on the value of breeding for hardiness in cultivated plants.

Farming in Natures Image, Piper and Soule, Island Press, 1990. Can a self sustaining, grain—producing ecosystem be designed like the prairie? If so what might be the components of such a system, how would it endure and what will it produce?

The Unsettling of America, Wendell Berry, North Point Press reprint, 1980. His sad, angry and accurate comments on the history and consequences of the ruin of the American countryside by a system of agriculture friendly to none of the living elements of the farm or landscape.

The New Agrarians edited by Eric Freyfogle, Island Press Shearwater book, 2001. A collection of articles and papers about the spirit and practice of modern agrarianism with contributions from Vandana Shiva and Wendell Berry Edited by **Eric Freyfogle**.

Arboriculture, Richard Harris, Prentice Hall Publications 1983. The A to Z of tree culture with extensive sections on planting, propagation and pruning by **Richard W. Harris** of the University of California at Davis.

Biomimicry, Janine Benyus, Perennial Press/Harper Collins Publishers, 1997. Learning agriculture,economy, logic and design from natural systems.

Plant Propagation, Principals and Practices by Hartman, Kester, Davies and Geneve, Prentice Hall, 1997. A book that explains ordinary plant propagation as well as grafting, budding, air layering plus pruning shaping and planting.

The Biology of Plants edited by Raven, Evert, Eichorn, Freeman and Worth Publications 1999. An immensely useful definitive basic text on the biology of the plant kingdom.

Non Timber Forest Products edited by **Marla Emery** and **Rebecca McLain. Food Products Press/Haworth Press, New York, 2001.** A collection of articles dealing with wild medicinal herbs, wild nuts, edible fungi and tree fruits and VAP products all from the forests of North America.

The Lost Crops of Africa vol. 1. edited by Noel Vietmeyer of the National Academy of Sciences National Academy Press, 1996. A truly remarkable study of underexploited, lost and wild grain crops. I am eagerly awaiting Vol 2. of this series which is dedicated to fruits and vegetables.

Saline Agriculture, edited by Griffin Shay, National Academy Press 1990 a small gem of a book from the **National Academy of Sciences** covering many aspects of saline agriculture and identifying crop candidates for arid and saline areas.

Underexploited Tropical Plants with Promising Economic Value edited by Noel Vietmayer and Julian Engel, National Academy Press, 1975. One of the first books written by the NAS dealing with new crops and crop candidates. Fascinating reading and still useful even though the book was first printed in 1975.

The Lost Crops of the Incas, edited by Noel Vietmeyer and Mark Dafforn, National Academy Press, 1988, full of interesting photographs and information about new and old crops including many pages of little known facts about the potato, the passionfruit and the relatives of the tomato.

The Gift of Good Land, Wendell Berry, North Point Press, 1986. Anecdotes and meditations about farming as a way of life in a century when land is considered a sterile media, farms are run like factories and farmers are considered unnecessary.

Enduring Seeds by **Gary Nabhan, North Point Press, 1984.** A psalm to the importance of biodiversity in agriculture.

The Soil and Health, Sir Albert Howard, Devon Adair, 1947. The theory and practice of organic agriculture explained by a man considered to be the father of modern organic agriculture.

Farming for Health and Disease, Sir Albert Howard, Devon Adair, 1945. An examination of the consequences of chemical farming to the soil and the population of human beings and animals dependent on the bounty of the soil. Both books are out of print. Both are absolute treasures. Look in libraries that have not thrown out their horticultural books from fifty years ago. Read and learn.

The Non Wood Forest Product Publications of the FAO.

These collections of research papers and compilations of proceedings from conferences on non wood forest products must be mentioned specifically because they are truly gold mines of information for the researcher dealing with IFT.

Packed with statistics and references the Non Wood Bulletins are sometimes the only sources of information about the rarer wild crops and the more obscure cultivated plants of economic importance. The Non Wood bulletins are not limited to taxonomy and horticulture either but deal with a wide range of subjects including marketing, processing, wildlife concerns, resource assessment, domestication and commercialization of Non Wood Forest Products as well as social change, village organization, education and conservation of genetic resources.

Websites

If a book is like a trusty companion during the years required to write an original manuscript—then these relatively new sources of information are very like rest stops and filling stations along the way.

I am referring to websites, extremely valuable pools of instant information that cannot take the place of the written word but certainly can provide concentrated facts and visual images relating to almost any subject.

The websites of these organizations are especially fertile ground for the IFT researcher or farmer

MAB, UNESCO's Man and Biosphere site

NTFP The website of the Non Wood Forest Product division of the FAO

ECHO—networking global hunger solutions

REHAB—The reforestation/agroforestry site of CIFOR—CGIAR

ICRAF International Center for Research in Agro-forestry

ICRISAT The International Crop Research Institute for the Semi Arid Tropics

NRET The Natural Resources and Ethical Trade site

INEF International Network of Ethnoforestry

IPALAC International Program for Arid Lands Crops

IUFRO International Union of Forestry Research Organizations

UNESCO United Nations Educational Scientific and Cultural Organization

IFRI International Forestry Resources and Institutions

AID Agency for International Development, USA

NAS The National Academy of Sciences, USA

TRAFFIC Trade Records and Analyses of Flora and Fauna in Commerce

ICBG the International Cooperative Biodiversity Group

DFID—Forest Research Program of the Department of International Development

FSC—Forest Stewardship Council

CITES Convention On International Trade in Endangered Species of Wild Fauna and Flora

ETFRN European Tropical Forest Research Network

WWF World Wide Fund for Nature

IUCN World Conservation Union

There are many other websites and webpages that may be helpful and more are being posted every year. It is impossible to name them all.

Googling the IFT species or wild crop will be helpful and will lead to other websites and web pages that may supply valuable information or facilitate contact between farmers and researchers who are working with the plant.

Local resources

Do not neglect local resources

A local gatherer of wild crops, a berry picker or tree tapper or even someone who simply roams the woods with a sharp eye can be an extremely rich source of information relative to wild edible IFT species especially regarding the locations of superior wild trees and the seasonal availability of IFT products.

Local farmers and gardeners also may be familiar with IFT species or be able to tell where they might be found, and how they might be used and cultivated. Local archives sometimes contain descriptions of preliminary agricultural experiments livestock feeding with IFT products and sketches of original wild populations.

Local forestry services and ranger stations may be able to describe an IFT species native range and pass on information regarding population density and importance to wildlife.

The information needed might be found in a book, or a website or in a conversation with another person who sups at God's table.

The IFT researcher will have to glean it from where it is found until the subject of IFT has been better described, documented and explored.

A process that, at the time I am writing, has barely begun.

Chapter Twenty-One
Towards A Diverse, Perennial
Agriculture

"Rain follows the plow." *proverb during the western expansion in the US*

"Civilized man has marched across the earth and left a desert in his footprints." *a more recent opinion*

Many people who work in the environmental sciences agree with the latter accurate and haunting quote.

Despite the best efforts of dedicated farmers and concerned scientists, even with the help of NGOs and national governments.. it is still true:

It is not *rain* that follows the plow but *ruin.*

Agriculture too often brings terminal land degradation in its wake and with it all the human suffering of famine, displacement and grinding poverty.

What is it that humanity does not understand? Why do the efforts of so many to raise up food out of the earth end in ecological disaster and human hunger?

There are fundamental errors in many agricultural systems that seem to make disaster inevitable.

A study of these mistakes and misunderstandings would fill many volumes.

But if the domestication and utilization of IFT is to be a new kind of agriculture, one that does not repeat the mistakes of the past, some of these mistakes must be mentioned and put in the context of IFT development.

The Agriculture of Displacement: Plains vs. Hills

The major food crops of the world, providing more than 80% of the food energy for man and beast, are the cereals, the soybeans and the potato crops. Cereals and soybeans are annuals and potatos while biennial are raised as annuals.

These are crops which must build themselves anew each season and in doing so require immense amounts of water, fertilizer and care.

Cultivated cereals are relatively weak plants on a competitive level and their bounty of grain can only be reaped efficiently if they are planted on clean flat, well tilled earth with clods broken up and possible competitors eliminated.

In other words this is the agriculture for thick layers of topsoil, plowed meadows and alluvial plains. The new powerhouse of nutrition, the soybean, is cultivated in much the same matter as well as corn, cotton, rape seed and a dozen other megacrops of the modern world.

Other than scope, chemicals and machinery, this kind of agriculture has not changed in thousands of years. It depends on plowing the land and making it bare, turning over the earth and making it vulnerable. Just this single act is enough to cause the erosion of hundreds of thousands of tons of topsoil every year.

Most of the crops modern agriculture promotes and almost all of the crops that fuel the economy are cultivated in this manner.

But now there are simply not enough areas in the world suitable for this kind of planting and cultivation. So as demand for these crops grows and grows the agriculture of the fertile, well watered plains, as ancient as Sumer, is displaced into hill land, sloping land, rocky areas, where trees and forests grow.

So the forests go down for timber and the stumps are burned.

Under the plow the deforested area makes a few good crops. But the thin hill soils are not renewed by the silt of rivers or the decay of stands of grass as the soils of the meadows are. There have never been meters of topsoil here in the hills—only a few precarious centimeters.

The humus and organic material in the hill soil is used up, the soil wears out, the crops fail and the area is abandoned.

The soil is then too poor to support the regrowth of the forest. Some land will go back to brush and weeds but much of it will erode away leaving gullies and desolation.

The entire process from forest to farm to wasteland may take less than sixty years.

This flatland system is so destructive when applied to hill regions because the agriculture of the plains has been transplanted to the margins, the mountains and the slopes, **unmodified.**

The differences in the depth of topsoil, its particular textures, the way the topsoil is formed and how it is renewed are all ignored by a misapplied cultivation protocol.

The vulnerability of such areas when plowed, with wind and gravity are at work, has never been properly addressed. Contour plowing, swales, swards and copses can mitigate the process by leaving areas of natural vegetation, moisture storage and catchment. But modern agricultural systems usually ignore both conserving measures and topography.

Most modern agricultural systems ignore proper rotation practices as well, eschewing fallows, green manures and regenerative crops and attempting to maintain fertility with chemicals instead.

If areas are not suitable for plains type agriculture by modern agricultural logic than obviously these areas have to be made over to **make** them suitable.

This attitude reached the point of absurdity in a 1970 National Geographic magazines hymn of praise to 20th century farming in which it was assumed that hills and other troublesome features of the landscape would be rendered flat as boardroom tables by atomic power. This was to be done so that farm machinery, even larger than the wheat harvesting monster combines, could roam about unrestricted, directed by remote control from airport style control towers miles away.

It is rarely pointed out that it is more logical, much less costly from an environmental point of view and cheaper in relation to human effort to leave the hills and mountains as they are and change instead the kind of agriculture we do.

Displacement of Agriculture to Deserts

There is a certain inevitability to the displacement of agriculture that accompanies urban development

Cities are founded on or very near good agricultural land As the cities grow the good land they were founded to serve disappears beneath roads, homes and buildings. Agriculture is pushed further and further away by the rising property values of the urban center.

While this is a distressing enough phenomena in areas with abundant arable land in the ancient lands around the Mediterranean displacement sometimes means moving agriculture into areas that are marginally arable or not arable at all.

In Israel and Jordan, for instance, the northern part of each country enjoys a Mediterranean climate and level of rainfall. The southern part of both countries is desert. The swift growth of towns and cities and ambitious road building programs in both countries has pushed agricultural projects further south. In Israel the desolate Arava valley south of the Dead Sea has become a center for the cultivation of winter vegetables while the Northern Negev has become a center for the cultivation of olives and vines. A similar pattern of displacement is appearing in Jordan.

Deserts are even less suitable for modern farming than hills. Fragile soils are compacted by machinery, salinized to ruin by irrigation, depleted quickly of minerals and organic material.

When abandoned the desert does not return to its normal state but remains in its degraded condition so bereft of positive qualities that it is called *desert pavement.*

Unfortunately there are large tracts of desert pavement in mis—cultivated arid areas all over the world.

As in the case of plains agriculture misapplied to the hills, Mediterranean agriculture applied to the deserts is costly and ultimately unsustainable.

The domestication and utilization of IFT species can be the basis for an ecologically sound agriculture more appropriate for mountains and deserts

Chemical Fertilizer

Since the time that Justus Von Liebig invented chemical fertilizer to the present day much attention has been paid to the chemical content of the soil. If a certain percentage of nitrogen, phosphorus or potassium is present the soil is declared to be fertile. The process in which these dead minerals become a part of the web of life is more or less ignored. It is almost as if the modern agriculturalist believes that if all the necessary chemical elements are present fertile soil will somehow assemble itself.

This is almost as logical as putting all the parts of a watch in a paper bag, shaking them up and expecting the watch to put itself together.

Fertile soil does not happen, it is made.

A list of all the types of creatures that turn dead stone into living soils and living tissue is beyond the scope of this book.

But they can be grouped into several types of organism, fungi (including the benign mycelium of mycorrhizal associations) bacteria, protozoa, insects, arthropods and mollusks.

All of these creatures are involved in breaking down organic matter into its most basic components and making these elements usable for associated organisms.

Without these tiny workers soil cannot be made. Leaving their well being out of the agricultural equations means that soils are not made, they are only used.

In too many agricultural projects and systems soils are used—then used up.

The soils dry out, lose their cohesion, lose their populations of worms and benign micro organisms and blow away on the unforgiving wind.

Or they become the dead hydroponic media that modern agriculture holds them to be.

This is the third major mistake that must not be reprised in IFT based agriculture.

IFT agriculture must be done in a way that is mindful of the process of soil making and not merely its use and chemical content.

Feeding Bread to the Animals

An uncomfortably high percentage of food crops are fed to animals. This includes, corn wheat, soybeans and oil seeds.

The animals do not need these foods, they are equipped to digest grass leaves, browse stubble and many other substances that keep them healthy—substances that people cannot eat.

Domestic animals, built to roam and graze in herds, are confined to vast feedlots where they can hardly move. Dosed with antibiotics to keep them safe from the diseases of overcrowding and fed constantly, they fatten very quickly.

After they are butchered, their fat marbled chemical laced meat is fed to increasingly unhealthy and obese citizens of the developed world who reap the results of this practice in the form of heart attacks, clogged arteries, strokes and other weight related diseases.

Meanwhile there are also an uncomfortably high number of people who cannot find, beg or buy their daily bread.

Over—cultivated crops, misused land, unhappy animals and people who are starving to death or dying of surfeit is the result of giving food suitable for humans to the animals.

Is there *anything* about this system that makes sense?

Why not replant the devastated, eroded, abandoned areas of the countryside with species of trees that provide high protein pods and browse thereby providing food for the animals **and** reforesting abandoned land?

Why not allow the animals to graze, browse and roam, eliminating many of the diseases of overcrowding and the need for drugs **and** producing leaner meats **and** reaping the benefits of better prices for healthier products?

And finally why not drop the expensive practice of subsidizing the production of grain so that the farmers of the developing world can grow their own crops for human consumption and not have to compete with the floods of cheap corn grown for the bellies of cows?

This complex web of destructive practices has to be unraveled sometime.

It should be done while there is still choice about how and when we do it and government money available to help the farmers, animals and consumers adjust.

Many trees suitable for animals feeding have already been identified among IFT species.

A modest program to promote IFT species as an element in the reform of modern animal feeding is essential and may have far—reaching influence and benefits.

The Misapplication of Vertical Resistance

The fifth major mistake that must not be made or remade in relation to the cultivation of IFT is monocropping and all its attendant errors of understanding.

The forest and the jungle are green and self sustaining and self perpetuating in a way no project of man can ever be.

To successfully cultivate IFT we must mimic some of the elements of the ecosystem.

Finding a Cinderella tree, cloning it a hundred thousand times and planting in a continuous orchard is **not** the way to utilize IFT.

The plants in a successful IFT based crop system must be diverse in cultivars and diverse within cultivars to prevent the build up of pests and parasites.

Many of the problems with pests in conventional agricultural systems stem from the poor soil health that plagues modern plantings.

But others are the result of a plant breeding and plant evaluation system that worships immunity and ignores hardiness.

In a wild ecosystem there are many tolerances and resistances among the plants.

Insect infestations and diseases can only do limited amounts of damage and even this damage nudges the system toward increased hardiness.

In a crop pathosystem, reduced to one kind of plant and sometimes only one variety of that one kind of plant, immunity can only be valid until a mutation or shift in the parasitic population overcomes it

Like the proverbial burglar who comes to town with one key but finds that it opens every lock in every home, the pest population that overcomes immunity in a monocrop is transported from a system that contains only obstacles to one that contains only opportunities.

An immunity or lock is meant to function as one of many immunities in a complex system of many locks and many resistances.

Moncocropping cancels the best and first line of plant defenses, like the houses with identical locks, the mathematics of the situation are no longer on the side of the plants.

Sucessful IFT planting does not need the plow, the spray gun or the orchard row.

An IFT based system with resistances of species intact should be planted in biomimicry of the jungle and forest with species integrated, varied and dispersed over unmauled topography.

Finding the components of a Perennial Agriculture in IFT

J. Russel Smith author of Tree Crops, A Permanent Agriculture envisioned a new type of agriculture dedicated to conserving the integrity and fertility of mountain soil and based on the cultivation of perennial plants.

He assumed that trees and minor perennials would be the mainstays of mountain farms with grain crops, legumes and vegetables gown in areas bordered, defined and protected by trees. He also assumed that orchard crops and grass crops would be part of a long term crop rotation with the trees drawing up needed minerals from the subsoil and making them available in the form of leaf litter and grass crops building up a layer of humus.

Perennial plants, in his opinion, are like great pumps bringing up subsoil water and subsoil minerals and allowing the lesser plants and animals and man access to these valuable substances.

Sir Albert Howard, British advocate of organic gardening and sustainable agriculture had a similar vision. His studies of agricultural systems made the link between disease in plants, animals and human beings to food crops grown in poor, humus—depleted de—mineralized soil.

J. Russel Smith was a Professor of Economic Geography at Columbia University. Sir Albert Howard was one of the first scientists to accurately describe mycorrhizal associations.

Their books are now out of print, their concerns made light of and their advice ignored.

There is no special school of mountain agriculture (though some progress has been made). A new agriculture based on perennial crops is still a dream, as it was in 1950 when J. Russel Smith published his book.

Sir Albert wrote of the links between the health of human beings and the health of the soil between 1921 and 1955.

The link between disease and agricultural practice is only now coming to the attention of the medical profession after a series of scandals from 1990 to 2005 involving prion diseases, bacterial contamination, contamination with toxic materials, unsuitable GM organisms in the human food chain and nutrition—less irradiated foodstuffs.

These two ignored voices from the past and many others whose work has never been taken seriously can point the way to a new kind of agriculture.

In the cultivation, development and conservation of IFT, farmers and researchers have the opportunity to avoid the mistakes of the past.

Proper cultivation and planting protocols can insure that new tree crops stay in areas suitable for them.

In crop diversity and sensible crop rotation combined with the hardiness of most IFT species will eliminate the need for pesticides.

Integration with annual crops, grass crops and animals husbandry will eliminate the need for herbicides.

The nourishment for tree, plant, beast and man in the IFT chain must come from the breakdown of organic matter in full cooperation with the mycorrhiza, soil insects and soil bacteria. IFT cultivation's goal should be the production of healthy food accomplished with full recognition of the importance of healthy soil.

IFT cultivation, a science in its infancy, can be taught and designed from the ground up in ways that protect the land, the IFT species, the domestic animals, the wildlife and the people who use love and depend upon the bounty of these wild trees.

Many modern agricultural practices cannot be corrected because of the tremendous economic pressures upon the people involved in the agricultural systems.

With billions of dollars at sake it is extremely difficult to make even minor reforms in the cultivation of cotton or corn.

There are no such economic stakes of pressures in the development and study of IFT.

The farmer and researcher is still free to look for the best way to proceed—the right way.

And to break the terrible cycle of misapplied skills, displaced crops, ruined land and hungry people.

Glossary

Abcisse—the separation and fall of fruit, flowers, leaves and other plant parts

Agricultural pyramid—the sides of the agricultural pyramid are: plants, farmers, animals, soil

Allele—different versions of the same gene, sometimes in the same organism

Amalou—traditional nut butter from Morocco made of ground almonds and argania oil.

Arable soil—soil that is suitable for agriculture

Artificial manure—the original name for chemical fertilizer

Bioinnoculants—cultures of bacteria and soil symbionts added to compost

Biometric School—the school of plant genetics dedicated to population breeding

Biopiracy—the act of stealing a material, plant or animal from its community of origin

Biosphere—the earth and all living elements upon it

Biotechnology——the science of accelerated, transgenetic manipulation of living creatures

Breeding—Controlled propagation of plants to achieve specific purposes

Cash crops—crops which are cultivated to supply raw materials in return for cash payment

Cloches—frames covered with glass or plastic to raise the air temperature around plants

Clones—offspring that are genetically identical to the parent plant

Cold bed agriculture—a system in which plants are nourished with cold water

Companion planting—the planting of different cultivars which benefit from each other's proximity

Compost—broken down, rotted plant material suitable for inclusion in the farm nutrient cycle

Conventional agriculture——agriculture based on the use of fossil fuels, chemical salts and monocrops

Conventional breeding processes—pedigreed breeding resulting in huge stands of identical plants

Crop diversity—multiple cultivars on a farm, multiple varieties within a cultivar

Crop rotation—planting crops is planned succession to curtail insect activity and preserve fertility

Cultivars—cultivated, domesticated plants

Cultivated—raised purposefully by the farmer or agriculturalist, worked by the farmer

Deciduous—loses leaves in the winter

Dioecious—Male and female flowers found on different plants of the same species

Domestication—the process by which the breeding and propagation of a wild organism comes under human influence

Dormancy—a state of inactivity or suspension of biological processes

Drip irrigation—irrigation systems which deliver precise amounts of water through small pipes

Ecotypical cultivar—a strain of crop plants well adapted to a specific locale

Epistasis—one gene modifies the expression of another gene, not an alelle of the first

Extractivist—a person whose profession is the extraction of useful materials from the wild

Exudates—Gums that are exuded naturally when bark of a gum producing tree is incised

Field resistance—enduring, non—specific, polygenetic tolerance of disease or environmental challenge

Gene pirates—nickname for biotechnologists who specialize in finding and patenting genes

Gene transfers—the transfer of genetic material to a different organism's genome

Genetic base—the gene pool of a crop plant

Genetic diversity—the variability and flexibility of a crop's gene pool

Genetic engineering—genetic modification, GM

Genetic imperialism—hunting and using genes from the developing world without giving payment or credit

Genetic modification—manipulation of the genome of an organism by the addition of exogenes

Genome—the complete complement of genes within an organism

Genotypes—, an organism with a specific genetic make—up—two organisms with the same genome are said to have the same genotype

Germinate—to sprout or develop

Germplasm—germ cells and bearers of heredity

Grafting—the technique of implanting tissue from one plant in the stock of another plant

Gray water—urban but non—industrial waste water, mostly from private dwellings

Growth inhibitors—substances that keep a seed from sprouting

Halophytes—salt loving or salt tolerant plants

Harvest index——the proportion of a crop which can be used for the crop's principle purpose

Hedgerows, useful plants and minor fruit crops planted to make a fence, barrier, windbreak moisture reservoir or shelter for wildlife between different features of agricultural landscapes.

Heel—part of a heeled cutting which has a piece of tissue from the trunk of the parent plant

Heirloom variety—older variations of cultivated plants with specific characteristics, now becoming rare

Hybrids—the progeny of a cross between two different varieties

IFT—Indigenous Fruit Tree

IWT—Indigenous Wild Tree

Indigenous—native to an area

Industrial style farming—high input, high energy use factory style farming

Integrated crops—crops and crop successions which are planted together for synergistic benefits

Integrated pest management—limiting pest populations by good farm management,

Intercrop—growing two or more cultivars together for their mutual benefit

Isolines—static and uniform end result of pedigreed breeding

Jaggery—drink made of tree sap, often fermented

Kamaradin—fruit leather VAP product

Landraces—primitive ecotypical cultivars, with great genetic variability and diversity

Legumes—a plant in the pea or bean family, usually capable of fixing nitrogen

Mendelian School—the pedigreed school of plant breeding

Modified seeds—seed which has undergone genetic manipulation

Monocrops—crops which are not genetically diverse, frequently the only cultivar in a wide area

Monoculture—the practice of growing large stands of one kind of identical plant

Mycorrhiza—fungal soil symbiont microorganisms

NFTC—Nitrogen Fixing Tree Crops

NWFP—Non Wood Forest Products

Operculum—lid or covering flap over a natural opening in a hard seed

Organically grown crops—crops which are raised in healthy soil without chemicals of any kind

Parasitize—to become a parasite upon another living organism

Patented genes—genes which are 'owned' by companies, individuals or institutions

Pattern rotation—a sophisticated form of crop rotation which curtails pests and disease

Perennial—a plant which lives for many years

Permaculture—the art/science of creating a stable, sustainable, humane, energy efficient food web

Phenotype—literally the physical characteristics of an organism

Phyto—pesticides—target materials derived from plants i.e. Neem

Plant clones—identical plants produced asexually

Pleiotrophy—effect of a gene on the expression of a number of different genetic traits

Polyunsaturated—oil or fatty acid rich in unsaturated bonds

Propagation—the breeding and multiplication of living organism

Reclamative crop—a crop which is planted to improve impoverished soil

Relic crop—a rare ecotypical cultivar, a surviving 'lost crop'.

Resistant varieties—plants which demonstrate non—specific or field resistance

Riparian systems—relating to or involving a watershed

Rootstock—the lower, rooted part of a grafted tree chosen for hardiness and tolerances

Saponins—any of various glucosides found in plants

Scion—the upper part of a grafted tree chosen for product characteristic

Sieman—measure of salinity

Seed bank—an institution dedicated to the preservation and storage of seeds

Shamba—ancient form of permaculture where trees support and shelter a mini—ecosystem of useful and edible plants, variation, cloud gardens, food forests

Shelf—life—the amount of time a food or product remains edible before spoilage

Soil building crops—crops which improve the health and fertility of the soil

Species—a class of individual organisms having common attributes and designated by the same name

Subsistence agriculture—agriculture in which families and villages provide food for themselves

Sustainable agriculture—agriculture that does not damage soil, water or farm environment

Synergistic integration—farm elements that enhance the health and productivity of other farm elements

Tertiary foods—herbs, spices, tea, coffee, cola and chocolate

Tilth—cultivation of the soil, the soil's suitability for cultivation

Transgene—gene from a dissimilar organism

Transgene traits—traits acquired by transferring genes from another organism

Tubers—thickened underground stems of a plant

VAP—value added products such as jam, kamaradin, liquor, teas

Vermiculite—water absorbing soil amendment used in nurseries

Wildcrafting—sustainble collection of wild plant products

Wildcrop—plant product which is not taken from cultivated plants but gathered from the wild

Wild pathosystems—in which each plant is different so the spread of disease is curtailed by variability

Windbreak—a line of trees or vegetation planted to reduce the force of the wind

Withies—flexible branches used for crafts usually from willow trees or other trees that grow along the water

Xiji—the familial territory for gathering gum of the frankincense tree

Figure 3: An IFT Introduction Site in Zimbabwe   (Elaine Solowey)

Figure 4: A Format for Domesticating Wild Viny Plants   (Elaine Solowey)

Figure 5: A Local Integration Sheltered by Date Palms   (Elaine Solowey)

Figure 6: Argania Trees in Orchard Format   (Elaine Solowey)

Figure 7: "Included" Argania Trees in Agaudir, Morocco   (Elaine Solowey)

Figure 8: Wild Argania Trees in the Atlas Mountains   (Elaine Solowey)

Figure 9: Mesquite Trees Grown for Fodder   (Elaine Solowey)

Figure 10: High Desert Lama and Vicuna Farm with Fodder Trees in Background

(Elaine Solowey)

Figure 11: IFT in the Farmyard, Zimbabwe

(Elaine Solowey)

Figure 12: Baobab Tree by the Zambezi River (Elaine Solowey)

Figure 13: Neem Trees Used as Shade Trees (Elaine Solowey)

Figure 14: The Quandong Tree (Yael Gilmor)

Figure 15: The Zisiphus Tree in Orchard Format (Yael Gilmor)

Figure 16: Balanites Trees (Elaine Solowey)

Figure 17: Woodlots in Yorkshire (Geoffrey Hobson)

Figure 18: Fruit of the Zisiphuis Tree (Yael Gilmor)

Figure 19: The Huge Trunk of the Kaypok Tree (Elaine Solowey)

Figure 20: The Myrrh Tree (Johanees Kuntsch)

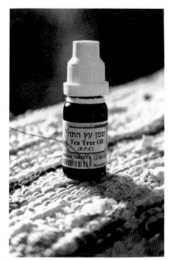

Figure 21: Medicinal Oil from the Ti Tree (Melaleuca.sp)   (Ruti Rubenstein)

Figure 23: A Simple Dryer for Teas and Medicinal Herbs   (Elaine Solowey)

Figure 22: Frankincense Sapling
(Johannes Kuntsch)

Figure 24: Seeds of the Balm of Gilead Tree
(Johannes Kuntsch)

Figure 25: Burls of a Forest Tree (Patricia Taylor)

Figure 27: Carob and Maple Syrup
(Ruti Rubenstien)

Figure 26: Marula Liquor (Ruti Rubenstien)

Figure 28: Argania Oil Produced in Israel
(Ruti Rubenstien)

Figure 29: Sampling Argania Oil, Amalou and Argan Honey in the Atlas Mountains

(Elaine Solowey)

Figure 30: Hedgerows, Wheatfields . and Pastures

(Geoffrey Hobson)

Figure 31: Hedgerows and Copses around a Wheat Field　(Geoffrey Hobson)

Figure 32: Wild Fruit Trees Protect a Field of Grain in Zimbabwe　(Elaine Solowey)

Index

saline soils 190
salinization 183
salt tolerant plants 191
salting 156
saps 100, 159
scion 114, 115
sea buckthorn 86
second domestication 48
seed recalcitrance 143
shambas 10, 37, 189
shea 72, 93, 112
shea butter tree 136
short seed viability 135
side tongue grafts 121
side veneer grafting 122
simple layering 132
smokewoods 161
snails 101
softwood cuttings 131
soil symbionts 136
splice grafting 121
sponges 160
starch 97
stewardship 177
stub grafting 121
suckers 118
sugar palm 99
sustainable livelihoods 63
sweet chestnut tree 68
syrups 100, 159

T

tamarind 77
tea tree oil 93
tenure 33

The International
  Convention on
  Biological Diversity 110
tilth 170
toddies 159
top dressing 145
topworking 113, 123
traditional agrarians 180
treetap 95
tropical soils 188
truffles 74, 101, 156

U

utility tree 69

V

V. paradoxa 137
Value Added Products
  (VAP) 4
VAP products 152
Vertical Resistance 208

W

whip and tongue grafts 119
white walnut 104
wild crafting 7
wild crops 8, 35
wild genotypes 17
willow 80
willow water 130
windbreaks 41, 69, 84
wines 159
withies 100, 160
woodlots 84, 172

X

xiji 35

Z

Made in the USA
Middletown, DE
18 July 2023

35376702R00142